She could **response** **body, and** **too.**

She wanted him to draw her closer, to know what it was like to be in his arms, his lips on hers, his hands caressing her—possessing her.

'I'm not the one to take you down that road,' Nick said softly, letting her go. 'Tempting proposition though it is.'

Erin drew in a mortified breath, the warmth rushing up under her skin. 'I don't know what you're talking about,' she said, attempting to infuse a genuine-sounding bewilderment.

The smile was brief. 'Yes, you do. It was coming from you in waves. Considering your lifestyle up to now, I'm probably the first male you've ever been in close enough contact with to light the spark. You'll soon get over it.'

She should be grateful, Erin supposed, that he had let her down so gently. Another man might have taken advantage of her girlish passions. A temptation, he had said; she wondered if he had really meant it or was simply pandering to her ego.

Kay Thorpe was born in Sheffield in 1935. She tried out a variety of jobs after leaving school. Writing began as a hobby, becoming a way of life only after she had her first completed novel accepted for publication in 1968. Since then, she's written over fifty and lives now with her husband, son, German Shepherd dog and lucky black cat on the outskirts of Chesterfield in Derbyshire. Her interests include reading, hiking, and travel.

Recent titles by the same author:

CONTRACT WIFE
THE THIRTY-DAY SEDUCTION

VIRGIN MISTRESS

BY
KAY THORPE

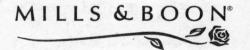

*First published in Great Britain 1999
Harlequin Mills & Boon Limited,
Eton House, 18-24 Paradise Road, Richmond, Surrey TW9 1SR*

© Kay Thorpe 1999

ISBN 0 263 81666 4

*Set in Times Roman 10½ on 11½ pt.
01-9905-52638 C1*

*Printed and bound in Norway
by AIT Trondheim AS, Trondheim*

CHAPTER ONE

'I'M AFRAID that's it,' said the solicitor with regret. 'The house is mortgaged up to the hilt, and what's left of the contents can be worth very little.'

'So I'll get a job,' Erin declared, grasping at straws. 'We'll manage!'

'At nineteen, with no particular qualifications, you'd find it difficult to obtain any employment that would provide you and your sister with an adequate living,' came the wry reply. 'It's fortunate that I was able to trace your uncle's whereabouts. He—'

'Samantha's uncle,' Erin cut in. 'I'm only a stepdaughter.'

'In the eyes of the law, that still makes you family. I'm sure Mr Carson will see it that way.'

If Nicholas Carson was anything at all like his brother, Erin reflected, he would probably be reluctant enough to assume responsibility even for Sam, who was at least his own kith and kin, much less herself, who was no relation whatsoever. Not that she wanted *anyone* assuming responsibility for her, if it came to that.

Mr Gordon was right, though, she was bound to concede. Even if she could find a job, there was little if any chance of her being able to provide for the two of them. The thought of being parted from her half-sister was distressing, to say the least, but Sam's welfare had to come before any other consideration. If her uncle had refused point-blank to be involved in his late brother's affairs—as he might have done after so many years estrangement—she could possibly

5

have been taken into care. Anything had to be better than that!

Watching the play of expression across the young face opposite, John Gordon could only admire the girl's apparent fortitude. A typical teenager, he had judged on first seeing her—fair hair long and loose about features bare of makeup, slender body clad in jeans and sweater. Widely spaced and thickly fringed, the vivid blue eyes belied that impression, registering a strength of character in advance of her years.

'I don't think the receivers will be pressing for an immediate vacation of the house,' he added, getting back to the matter in hand, 'but the sooner you start sorting things out the better. It would probably be easiest to bring in a house clearance firm to give you an overall price on what's left of the furnishings, though Mr Carson will want to go through his brother's personal belongings himself, I imagine. He'll be here before the end of the week.'

By which time she would need to have some idea of her own movements, Erin concluded, although quite what she was going to do she had little real notion as yet. Somewhere to live would be a first priority.

Unexpected though it had been, her stepfather's death had left no particular void in her life. They had never been close at the best of times, and since her mother had gone they'd become even further apart. Not that he'd given his own daughter that much attention either. So far as David Carson had been concerned, the two of them were a liability he could well have done without.

'How did you manage to find Mr Carson?' she asked curiously. 'So far as I know, there hadn't been any contact between him and my stepfather for years.'

'The gallery where he exhibits in town put me in touch with his agent, who then got him to contact me.

Unfortunately, by the time he did, it was too late for him to make the funeral.'

'I don't suppose he felt it mattered whether he was there or not,' Erin murmured, trying to be impartial about it. 'He's quite well known, isn't he?'

'More than quite, I'd say,' returned the solicitor. 'I'm not into art myself, but his work is considered exceptional by those who are. He's still only young too.'

Maybe to him, thought Erin, but from her viewpoint thirty-four was already more than halfway over the hill! The ten years between the two brothers could have had a lot to do with the bust-up, she supposed. Nicholas wouldn't have been all that much older than she was now when he took off on his own. From what little she knew about it, there had been money involved. No surprises there. Money no doubt played as important a role in his life as it had in her stepfather's. It was losing it all that had caused the latter's heart attack, she was sure.

'Do you think Barbados is going to be a suitable place for a fourteen-year-old to live?' she asked. 'I mean, there's school, for instance.'

'By all accounts, schools on the island are as good as you'll find anywhere.' John Gordon hesitated. 'On the other hand, Mr Carson might see a good boarding-school as a better solution. After all, at his age, and unmarried, he's hardly in an ideal position to take on full-time supervision of a fourteen-year-old. I'm not even sure Barbados is his permanent home.' His voice briskened. 'Anyway, those are things to be decided when he gets here. I'm sure he'll do what's best all round.'

Erin only wished she could be as sure. Sam would hate boarding-school. Not that being transported thousands of miles to a new home among total strangers would be any picnic for her either. But there was no point getting in a twist about it at this stage, she told herself staunchly. No point getting in a twist about anything until they knew what was in store.

Held up by traffic, she was ten minutes late reaching the school, and was relieved to find her sister still waiting. Left to her own devices, Samantha was capable of begging a lift from any likely-looking source rather than take the somewhat roundabout bus route home, heedless of any possible danger.

Like Erin herself, she took after their mother in looks, fair hair caught up in a swinging ponytail, blue eyes vivid in a face just beginning to reveal the fine boning beneath. Erin had done her best to make up for the lack of parental caring, but there was no real substitute, as she knew to her own cost.

'I thought you were never going to get here!' the younger girl complained lightly, climbing into the car they were soon to lose along with the rest. 'What did Mr Gordon say?'

'Nothing we hadn't already worked out for ourselves,' Erin acknowledged, seeing no point in being anything but straight about it. 'It's all gone, Sam. House, money—everything.'

'Well, Dad never gave us much money, so that isn't going to make a lot of difference,' came the unperturbed response. 'Melanie says her mum gets money from the post office every week, and the council gave them a house. We could do the same, couldn't we?'

If it was only as simple as that, thought Erin wryly.

'I don't think our situation is quite the same,' she said. 'In any case, we have to find out what your uncle has in mind when he gets here. Officially he's your guardian. That means we have to do whatever he says.'

Samantha looked mutinous. 'I don't need a guardian! You've always looked after me. Why can't you now?'

'I don't have the means,' Erin acknowledged with an inner sigh. 'Your uncle has.'

'If he's got lots of money, he could buy us a new house!'

'There's a bit more to it than that, I'm afraid.' Erin sought an upbeat note. 'How about calling at Halson's for some chocolate eclairs?'

Blue eyes lit up. 'Can we afford them?'

'No, but who cares?' declared her sister recklessly. 'Let's live for the moment!'

They bought six, and devoured the lot at a sitting on reaching the house they could no longer regard as home. A five-bedroomed detached in this area should fetch a fair price, Erin considered as she washed up the tea things after they'd finished eating. Whether whatever it did fetch would be enough to clear her stepfather's debts was another matter. Hardly her concern anyway, thank heaven. She had other things to worry about.

The two of them spent a quiet evening watching television. Samantha took herself off to bed around ten without being urged for once, leaving Erin to mull over those same concerns without reaching any useful conclusions. In the words of one of her favourite fictional heroines, tomorrow was another day, she decided philosophically in the end. A good night's sleep, and everything would look better.

As so often happened, by the time she had got herself ready for bed she was wide awake again. With the idea that a cup of hot chocolate might help her sleep, she went down to the kitchen to heat some milk, not bothering to put on a dressing gown over her short cotton nightdress.

It had started to rain, she realised, hearing the patter against the kitchen window. Good for the garden, which was suffering from the unusually dry spring. Not that it was going to be her problem for very much longer, of course.

She had her foot on the bottom tread of the stairs when

she heard the sound of a car engine, along with the unmistakable crunch of tyres on the gravel drive. Headlights flashed across the glass panes of the outer door as the vehicle took the curve to draw up in front of the house.

There was a short pause, the sound of voices, then a dark shape loomed beyond the glass and the bell push was depressed with what Erin considered a totally unnecessary vigour, considering that a light was still on. There was only one person this caller could be, only one person they were expecting—though not quite this soon, it had to be admitted.

Setting the mug of chocolate down on the flat square top of the newel post, she padded across the carpet to open the door, fingers already sliding the bolt before caution took over and halted the motion. The figure out there was certainly male, but that was all she could be sure of.

'Who is it?' she asked.

'Nick Carson,' came the anticipated answer. 'Open up, will you? I'm getting wet out here.'

Rain tends to do that, it was on the tip of her tongue to retort, but she bit it back. This was no time to get smart. She finished sliding the bolt, and turned the key, drawing the door towards her with more than a little reluctance to admit the man who held Sam's immediate future in his hands.

He signalled to the taxi to go before stepping forward into the light, towering over her for a moment as he brushed past to deposit a suitcase on the hall floor. Closing the door again, Erin turned with her back to it in a stance instinctively wary as she viewed strongly carved features. Taller by two or three inches than her stepfather, who himself had been close to six feet, he resembled him only in the colour of his eyes, which were grey, and the thick dark hair. A stronger personality altogether, she judged, meeting the penetrative gaze. Whether that meant stronger in fibre was something else.

'Taking it that you're a mite older than fourteen,' he remarked, running an assessing glance over her, 'who exactly are *you*?'

'I'm Samantha's half-sister,' she said. 'Didn't Mr Gordon tell you about me?'

'I'd hardly be asking if he had,' was the dry response. 'All I got from him was that my brother had died, leaving a fourteen-year-old daughter without a penny. Half-sister, you say?'

'My mother married your brother when I was four. Sam was born the year after.'

He studied the dewiness of her skin, the soft curve of her mouth and the long, straight curtain of fair hair, his lips taking on a slant. 'I'd have gone for maybe sixteen rather than nineteen. Do you usually wander about the house in your nightdress?'

'Only at night,' she said, refusing to be self-conscious about a garment she knew was no more revealing than the average mini-dress. 'Lucky I came down for a drink. Otherwise I'd have probably been asleep by now.'

'In which case I'd have had to waken you.' He made an abrupt movement. 'There's obviously a whole lot I haven't been told. Supposing we go somewhere more comfortable? I've been travelling most of the day.'

'If you're tired, we could always leave things till morning,' Erin suggested hopefully, looking for a reprieve.

'We'll sort it out now,' he stated unequivocally. 'I need to know just what's expected of me.'

'So far as I'm concerned, nothing,' she assured him. 'I can take care of myself.' She started forward, pausing as a thought struck her. 'Did you want something to eat?'

He shook his head. 'I ate on the plane.' His glance

shifted to the mug resting on the newel post. 'Better bring that along before it goes cold.'

Erin went to retrieve it, toes curling into the carpet pile. She rarely wore shoes around the house, much less slippers, but she regretted the lack right now. Children ran about barefoot, not adults. No wonder this man doubted her age.

Stripped of all items of any real value, the living room looked denuded. Nick Carson made no comment, though his expression spoke volumes. Erin switched on a couple of lamps and turned off the overhead light in an effort to soften the effect, curling into a chair the way she usually did, with bare legs tucked under her, as her step-uncle—if there was such a title—took a seat on the sofa.

He was dressed fairly casually, she noted, though not in any arty fashion, the dark tan trousers and lighter cord jacket conservative, if anything, in cut. On the surface, not at all what she had anticipated, but there was a lot more to people than their outward appearance.

'What exactly do you intend doing about Sam?' she asked.

The directness of the question drew a lift of one dark brow. 'Not backward in coming forward, are you?'

'Not backward in anything, I hope,' she retorted, with no intention of allowing herself to be browbeaten. 'I'm naturally concerned about what's going to happen to her.'

'And what about you?'

'I've told you, *I* can take care of myself.'

'Does that mean you already have plans made?'

Erin lifted her shoulders in a gesture meant to convey a total lack of concern. 'Nothing specific as yet.'

'You have money of your own?'

'No,' she was bound to admit, much against her will. 'But I can always get a job.'

'Doing what exactly?'

'Children's nanny, for instance,' she improvised, unable

to think of anything else on the spur of the moment. 'A live-in nanny,' she added, warming to the idea.

'Without qualifications or experience?'

Blue eyes held grey unwaveringly. 'I've had plenty of practice looking after Sam.'

'There's a lot of difference between keeping an eye on a kid sister and taking care of a child or children full-time,' Nick pointed out. 'You're hardly more than a kid yourself, if it comes to that.'

A spark lit the blue. 'It isn't just a matter of years. And kids, by the way, are young goats.'

'I stand corrected.' There was a hint of amusement in the brief widening of the firm mouth. 'Is Samantha as self-assured as you?'

Erin kept her tone easy with an effort. 'We can both stand up for ourselves, if that's what you mean. And you still didn't say what you intend doing about her.'

'I'm hardly going to be making any hard and fast decisions at this point,' he returned. 'As I said, there's a lot I need to know first. About your mother, for instance. What—?'

'She was killed in a plane crash a few years ago,' Erin interjected without emotion. 'Along with the man she was running off with, who was piloting it. I left school to keep house.'

'Your own idea, or my brother's?'

Slender shoulders lifted in another brief shrug. 'There wasn't much alternative.'

'He could have hired a housekeeper and allowed you to complete your education.'

'At a cost. Anyway, I didn't like the idea of some stranger taking over.' Still don't, she could have added.

'At least with me there's a blood tie,' he said, apparently able to read minds. 'Not that I'm in seventh heaven myself

over the situation. I'm surprised David would have bothered to name me as next of kin to start with.'

'He had to name someone, I suppose, and you're all there
is.' Erin hesitated, wondering if it was too soon to voice
the suggestion she had been turning over in her mind all
evening. Better sooner than later, she decided, though a
little subtlety wouldn't go amiss.

'I can understand how difficult it would be for you to
have Sam to live with you,' she began. 'I mean, being on
your own, and all that.'

There was a quizzical expression in the grey eyes. 'What
makes you so sure I live alone?'

'Mr Gordon said you weren't married.'

'And I'd have to be, of course, to have a woman living
with me?'

Erin bit her lip, feeling a complete idiot. How naive
could you get? She made an effort to cover up the mo-
mentary embarrassment, voice as toneless as she could
make it. 'So would your…partner be willing to accept a
fourteen-year-old addition to the household?'

'I didn't say I had one,' he returned. 'I've yet to meet
the woman I could live with full-time.'

'The problem might be finding a woman who could live
with *you* full-time!' Erin flung at him in sudden surging
antagonism.

'Possibly,' he agreed with infuriating calm. 'You were
saying?'

Erin took a hold of herself, already regretting letting fly
that way. There was something about this man that made
her feel all keyed-up and on edge, but giving way to it was
hardly going to help convince him of her fitness to be left
in full charge of his niece.

'I'm sorry,' she got out. 'I shouldn't have spoken to you
like that.'

'Why not?' he asked. 'You're entitled to say whatever

you like, providing it isn't slanderous.' The pause was pointed, the grey eyes too perceptive by half. 'You were going to suggest I consider leaving Samantha in your care, I believe? With some financial aid to boot, of course.'

'For her, not me.' Erin set herself to recover lost ground. 'And only until I was in a position to support us both. She's doing well at school,' she said, mentally crossing her fingers. 'It would be a shame to uproot her. We could rent a furnished flat for the time being—there are always plenty advertised in the paper.' Legs uncurled, she was poised on the edge of her seat, eyes fired with enthusiasm for her cause. 'It would be better for Sam, and for you too. It *has* to be!'

There was a certain calculation in Nick Carson's regard, as if he were weighing up what she had said. When he spoke, it was with dry deliberation. 'I think this would be better discussed in the morning after all—without the distractions.'

Having totally forgotten how she was dressed, it took Erin a moment to glean his meaning. Colour tinged her cheeks as she looked down to see the way her nightdress had ridden up, exposing a length of slender thigh.

'You do have *some* inhibitions, then,' he commented as she pulled the material hastily down again. 'I was beginning to wonder.'

'There wasn't much point in my coming all over coy when you'd already seen me,' Erin responded with what sangfroid she could muster. 'Anyway, I shouldn't have thought you'd find a bit of bare leg so hard to ignore—especially when it belongs to someone you see as little more than a kid!'

'I shouldn't have thought so either.' Nick sounded amused again. 'Nothing throws you for long, does it?'

'Not unless it's important.' She put up an automatic hand

to push the hair back from her face, wishing she had something handy to tie it with. 'So what do you think?'

'About what?'

Erin drew a hard breath, suspecting him of playing with her. 'About what I was saying just now, of course!'

'Oh, yes, your considered plan for the future.' He shook his head. 'No go, I'm afraid.'

'Why not?' she demanded, hopes crashing about her ears. 'If it's the cost, I'd guarantee to pay you back as soon—'

'It isn't about money.' His tone was peremptory. 'What you're proposing is a long way from what I'd consider a suitable solution to the problem.'

Erin looked at him helplessly, recognising adamancy when she heard it. Sitting there, broad of shoulder and square of jaw, he looked the proverbial immovable object, with her force, it seemed, far from irresistible.

'So what *would* you consider a suitable solution?' she asked.

The shrug was brief. 'We'll talk about it in the morning, after I meet Samantha herself.'

He got to his feet in one smooth movement, the open jacket revealing a lean hipline and taut waist. Gazing up at him, Erin was aware of a sudden stirring deep down in the pit of her stomach. She wasn't backward enough not to recognise physical chemistry at work, although she would never have anticipated feeling any attraction whatsoever towards a man of Nicholas Carson's age. He was almost old enough to be her father, for heaven's sake!

'I just realised I don't even know your name,' he said, snapping her out of it.

'Erin,' she told him. 'Erin Grainger.'

The dark brows drew together. 'Was it your own choice to keep your father's name?'

'Mother's name,' she corrected impassively. 'I never knew who my father was.'

'David could have adopted you.'

'He didn't want to. At least he never made any attempt. I imagine he felt he'd done enough marrying Mum.'

Nick's expression was difficult to judge. 'He must have had some feeling for her.'

'I suppose.' Erin rose abruptly, unwilling to discuss the matter any further. 'I'll need to make up the bed for you. Like I said, we weren't expecting you before the weekend. It will only take a few minutes.'

'I may as well come up with you, then,' he said. 'It isn't exactly a welcoming atmosphere down here.'

Erin could hardly deny it. She led the way, self-conscious as she climbed the stairs with him close at her back. The room he was to have was next door to her own. She paused on the way to take clean sheets and a duvet cover from the linen cupboard on the landing.

'I'm afraid there's little more than the basics left in here either,' she said apologetically, opening the bedroom door. 'I didn't know whether you'd want to go through your brother's things yourself, so I left everything as it was. His personal papers are in that suitcase in the corner. The study furniture went to auction.'

'So long as there's a mattress on the bed, I dare say I can manage,' Nick advised. 'I'll have a look through the paperwork in the morning, but the rest can go straight to charity.'

He dropped the travel bag he was carrying on the floor as Erin shook open the bottom sheet to spread it across the double bed, moving forward to take the far side and pull it straight meeting her surprised glance with an ironic smile. 'I'm not above lending a woman a hand with household chores on the odd occasion.'

'A woman now, am I?' she retorted, sensing ridicule. 'That's what I call quick promotion!'

'General terminology,' he returned smoothly. 'Sling the duvet cover across and we'll each tackle our own corners.'

Erin did so, irritated beyond measure when he completed his part of the task before her. Having had no help in the house these past three years, she was used to doing things her own way, and resented his interference. Resented his being here at all. They would have managed somehow without him.

Leaving one of her corners unfilled, in what she knew was a thoroughly childish gesture, she straightened to indicate the other door leading from the room. 'That's the *en suite* bathroom. You'll find towels in the cupboard.' She hesitated before adding, 'You do realise that apart from a few odds and ends there isn't going to be anything left?'

Nick inclined his head. 'I gathered as much. My brother was always one for putting his eggs in one basket. He was lucky to last as long as he did without coming to grief.' He left it there, lifting his shoulders in a dismissive gesture that suggested regret over having said as much as he had. 'I'll make a start in the morning. Right now, I'm all for getting my head down.'

It was gone midnight, Erin realised, catching a glimpse of the bedside clock that hadn't been deemed worth enough to bother with by the bailiffs. Sleep was the last thing on her mind all the same; there was far too much to think about.

'I'll leave you to it, then,' she said shortly. 'I'm usually up by seven, but don't feel obligated to do the same.'

She moved to the door, pausing there as a thought struck her. 'About Samantha? Did you want her to stay home from school tomorrow?'

'It might be an idea,' Nick agreed. 'Give us an opportunity to get to know one another.'

A day was hardly going to be long enough for that, it was on the tip of Erin's tongue to observe, but she bit it back. There was still a glimmer of hope that he would come round to seeing things her way in the end—especially after meeting Sam and realising she was far from the pliant little thing he probably visualised. Acting like a responsible adult herself would be a good start.

'We can both of us only be grateful that you didn't decide to opt out altogether,' she said. 'Some men would have done.'

Hoisting the travel bag onto the bed to open it, Nick gave a short laugh. 'You knowing so much about men, of course.'

Erin caught herself up before the pithy reply could take shape on her lips; she had a feeling she might be exercising more and more restraint over the coming few days.

'I count myself a fair judge of character,' she said levelly instead. 'I'm sure you must have had good reason to part company with my stepfather. See you in the morning,' she added swiftly, and closed the door before he could answer.

She'd left the hot chocolate downstairs after all that, she realised on the landing. Not that it would be hot any longer. She briefly contemplated going down again to reheat it, but doubted if it was going to help her get to sleep anyway.

What she needed to do was replan her whole approach—to convince that doubting Thomas in there that she was capable of making a life right here for Samantha. He didn't really want her himself; that was obvious. She couldn't blame him for it either. What confirmed bachelor in his thirties *would* welcome the idea of taking on a fourteen-year-old?

There was no sound from Sam's room. Finding her uncle already in residence when she got up was going to be a surprise, but she wasn't easily thrown. He might get a surprise himself when he met her, and realised just how adult she could be for her age.

Always providing, of course, that she didn't take an instant dislike to her only living blood relative and act accordingly. She could, Erin was forced to acknowledge, be a total brat when the mood came over her. An early warning might be advisable.

In her own room, she stood for a moment by the door, listening for any sound from the next room, but none reached her. He would be in the bathroom on the far side, she guessed. At least that was still fully equipped. She had a sudden mind's-eye vision of that tall, lean body stripped of all clothing, and felt that same curling sensation deep down in the pit of her stomach. She had seen the naked male form in art works, but this was a different feeling altogether.

He's old enough to be your father, a small voice reminded her. Unlikely, maybe, but certainly possible. She dismissed the image forcefully, settling instead on what she knew of his background. The brothers had been left equal shares in their father's estate. David had wanted the younger man to join him in business ventures, but Nick had refused and gone his own way. Erin couldn't lay any blame at his door for that; given the choice herself, she would have done the same. What she could neither understand nor condone was the total lack of contact between the two of them since.

For her stepfather to have failed to appeal for financial help during the final crisis was beyond understanding too; he had certainly tried every other avenue. Unless he had, of course, as a last resort, and been turned down. That thought hadn't occurred to her before.

Was the man next door capable of refusing to help his own brother out of desperate straits? Erin cogitated. He came across as a tough nut to crack, but would he really be that ruthless? Without asking him outright, she was hardly likely to ever know.

In bed, though far from sleep, she lay listening to the rain on the windows, wondering what the fates had in store. Life would be simpler, she supposed, if Nick Carson did take Samantha back to Barbados with him, but the parting would be hard.

Not that worrying about it was going to make any difference, she concluded wryly. The ultimate decision rested entirely with him.

CHAPTER TWO

THE alarm jerked Erin from a sleep that had held a quality of exhaustion. Stretching out a hasty arm, she switched the sound off, hoping it wouldn't have disturbed the occupant of the room next door. She needed to warn Sam before Nick put in an appearance.

As always, her sister was still dead to the world, head burrowed deep beneath the covers. She came awake with reluctance when urged, pulling an indignant face when she saw the time.

'It's only just gone seven!' she exclaimed grumpily. 'I don't get up till half past!'

'Usually,' Erin agreed. 'Today's different. We have a visitor.'

Samantha looked at her blankly for a moment, then in dawning realisation. 'He got here already?'

'Late last night.'

The younger girl sat up, all thoughts of sleep flown. 'So what's he like?'

'Tall, dark, and bossy.'

Samantha grimaced again. 'Sounds just like Dad!'

'Well, they are brothers.' Erin kept her tone light. 'He wants you to stay off school today so you can start getting to know one another.'

Blue eyes brightened immediately. 'Things are looking up already!'

Don't count on it, Erin wanted to tell her, but some things were better left unspoken. Sam would find out what was in store for her soon enough.

'It will look better if we're both of us up and dressed by

the time he surfaces,' she said instead. 'I'll take first shower, then I can be fixing breakfast while you get yourself organised. Just don't use the day off school as an excuse to go back to sleep again,' she added, knowing her sister only too well. 'If you're not out by the time I finish, I'll throw a jug of water over you!'

'You're the one who'll finish up with a load of wet bedding to deal with if you do,' was the prompt response.

Which was true enough, Erin conceded. She left her to it, and went back to her own room to collect some clothes before making for the bathroom. The master bedroom door was firmly closed. She hoped it would remain that way a good while longer.

It was a fine sunny morning after last night's rain. Erin felt her spirits lift when she opened the bathroom window to admit the myriad of scents of an English spring. Perhaps Uncle Nick would prove a little more amenable to suggestion after a good night's sleep. He might even have come to recognise the advantages for himself.

There was still no sign of movement from the newcomer's room when she emerged. Samantha, she was pleased to find on popping her head round the door, was actually out of bed and ready to take her place in the bathroom.

'Make it quick as you can,' she urged. 'I want to be finished eating before your uncle puts in an appearance. He'll probably want the works.'

'You could present him with the frying pan and let him do his own.' Samantha grinned at the look on her sister's face. 'Start as you mean to go on—isn't that what you're always telling me?'

Erin grinned back. 'Telling and doing are two different things. Anyway, he's hopefully not going to be here long enough for any patterns to be set.'

She clung to that thought as she headed for the stairs.

The last thing he was surely going to want was an extended stay. Time was in short supply in any case. The house had to be cleared before it was put on the market, and the bank wasn't going to wait much longer.

With breakfast the first thing on the agenda, she made straight for the kitchen, coming to a disconcerted stop in the doorway on seeing Nick Carson seated at the central table with a mug of coffee to hand and the daily newspaper she hadn't yet got around to cancelling propped against the coffeepot.

He looked up from his perusal of same on her entrance, taking in every aspect of the slender young body revealed by close-fitting jeans and a pale blue T-shirt.

'A bit more circumspect than last night's outfit,' he commented.

'People who drop in unexpectedly have to take as they find,' Erin returned, struggling to retain an outer composure at least. 'I didn't think you'd be up yet.'

'I was awake at six.' He looked beyond her. 'What time is Samantha likely to surface?'

'She'll be down in a minute.' Erin stirred herself to move on into the kitchen. 'Assuming you didn't eat yet, what would you like?'

'Cereals, fruit, and yoghurt, if you've got it, will do me fine.'

'I don't mind cooking you something, if you'd prefer it,' Erin offered. 'Your brother always had the works.'

'I'd prefer to live a little longer than he did.'

'You mean you're a health nut?'

A spark of humour lit the grey eyes. 'No, I'm not a ''health nut,'' as you so elegantly put it, just not too fond of fry-ups—especially first thing in the morning. The coffee's still hot if you want some to be going on with.'

He took her agreement for granted, reaching for a clean mug from the tree by his elbow. Seating herself on the far side of the table, Erin watched him refill his own mug, unable to restrain a faint snort when he spooned in sugar.

'We all have our weaknesses,' he said drily. 'Cheers!'

The coffee was a little too strong for Erin's taste, but she refrained from saying so. She was supremely aware of his comparative closeness—of the possibility of catching a foot against his outstretched ones. He was wearing jeans and T-shirt himself this morning, the latter revealing the muscular structure of chest and shoulders. For the first time since she had learned to speak, she found herself totally tongue-tied.

Nick regarded her with lifted brows as she continued to sit there mute. 'Not so much to say for yourself this morning!'

'I was waiting for you to start the ball rolling,' she claimed. 'There must be all kinds of things you need to know.'

The shrug was brief. 'I'd say you filled me in pretty well on the detail last night.'

Erin eyed him hopefully. 'Did you come to any definite decision yet?'

'With regard to what?'

'What I asked you to consider. I realise you'd be subsidising me too for a while, but I'd honestly—'

'I told you that idea was no go,' he said flatly. 'Nothing happened overnight to change my mind.'

She gazed at him in frustration. 'Then what *do* you plan on doing? Sam won't settle at boarding-school, I can tell you that now!'

The grey eyes acquired a suddenly steelier glint. 'She'll do whatever's decided for her.'

'I wouldn't bet on it!' Erin was too inflamed by the tone to pay any further lip service to diplomacy. 'You can't push a fourteen-year-old around!'

'Calm down.' It was said quietly enough, but the inflection left nothing to misinterpretation. 'You're doing neither of you any favours.'

Erin took a grip on herself. For a moment there he had reminded her so much of her stepfather. 'I'm concerned about her, that's all,' she said stiffly, unable to bring herself to apologise. 'Send her away to school and she'll probably finish up running away.'

Nick drew an impatient breath. 'I hadn't even thought about boarding-school till you threw it in my face just now.'

'So what's the alternative?' she demanded. 'As a bachelor, you can hardly have her to live with you on her own. Imagine how people would talk.'

'Tell me about it.' He paused, expression hard to read. 'I'm not going to try making out I'm over-enthused about acting as surrogate father to a fourteen-year-old, but, as you pointed out last night, I'm all there is, so it seems it's needs must—for the time being, at any rate. I'll be relying on you for support.'

Erin stared at him in silence for a lengthy moment, the wind taken completely out of her sails. 'You're suggesting that I come to Barbados too?' she got out.

The strong mouth slanted. 'Why the surprise?'

'It's supposed to be only women who answer one question with another,' she said, and saw the slant increase.

'When it comes to prevarication, your sex wins hands down! If you don't want to come, say so.'

'It isn't that simple,' she protested. 'Sam's kith and kin; I'd just be a...charity case.'

'You'd save me the trouble of finding someone else to act as nursemaid—or whatever you like to call it. That has to be worth your keep. As to the rest, you could always get a job.'

'Doing what? As you pointed out last night, I'm not qualified for anything.'

'Qualifications can be gained.'

'Given time. Up until then—'

'Up until then you could make yourself useful around the house if you feel that strongly about it.'

'*I'm* not going unless you come too,' stated Samantha from the doorway.

'*You* don't have any choice,' replied her uncle.

Blue eyes took on extra sparkle. 'Erin said you were bossy!'

'Erin doesn't know the half of it.' Impatience had given way to amusement. 'Hallo, Samantha. Easy to see which side you take after.'

She regarded him consideringly. 'Do I have to call you uncle?'

'Nick will do fine,' he said. 'Let's all be adults together.'

Her grin registered approval. 'Okay, Nick. I prefer Sam, by the way.'

'Now in that you *do* have a choice,' he returned equably.

'I'll get breakfast,' Erin declared, still unable to get her mind round the idea he'd just outlined to her. 'Juice, everybody?'

'You didn't give me an answer yet,' Nick reminded her. 'And, yes, I do want it now,' he added, guessing what she was about to say. 'I like things cut and dried.'

Considering that the only alternative was to wave goodbye to Sam for the foreseeable future and apply for support from the State while she looked for work, she'd be a fool to say no, Erin conceded. 'Then I suppose it's yes,' she said, with some hesitation still. 'And...thanks.'

The dark head inclined with a mockery directed as much at himself as at her. 'You're welcome.'

'So, having settled that much,' said Samantha, pulling out a chair for herself, 'when do we go?'

'At least it seems I can count on unmitigated enthusiasm

from one side of the family,' came the dry comment. 'Monday, if we can get a flight.'

Erin almost dropped the cereal bowls she had just taken from the cupboard. 'We can't possibly have everything done by then!'

'What doesn't get done gets left. All you need worry about is your personal stuff.'

'It isn't just the house. We neither of us have passports, for one thing.'

'A detail. We'll take a trip into town this morning.' Nick lifted a sardonic eyebrow as she made no move to carry on with what she was doing. 'Anything else?'

Erin attempted to get her thoughts in order. 'There's the school.'

'They'll be informed.'

'Considering it's Friday tomorrow, does that mean I needn't go back at all?' asked Samantha hopefully, giving vent to a cheer when he signified assent. 'Great stuff!'

'Don't get too carried away,' her uncle advised. 'You've still got a few years to go.' He turned his attention back to Erin again. 'That it?'

'More or less,' she acknowledged, unable to come up with any further delaying factor. 'I'm just not used to things happening so fast,' she tagged on lamely. 'You're very…decisive.'

'An improvement on "bossy," I suppose.'

Erin had to smile. 'You did come across a bit that way last night.'

'Put it down to jet-lag.' Nick looked meaningfully at the bowls she was still holding. 'Do we get to eat at all?'

'Right away.' Erin slid the bowls onto the mats already laid out, and turned to open another cupboard. 'Cornflakes okay?'

'Fine.'

Which was just as well, considering it was the only ce-

real they had in right now, she reflected. She would need
to pay a call at the supermarket to gather supplies to tide
them over the next few days. Hopefully, she had enough
cash to hand.

She took the same chair opposite Nick to eat her own
flakes. Seated beside her, Samantha kept up a lively conversation throughout the meal. Erin wished she could feel
as much at ease with the situation.

While her presence might be needed in order to stop any
possible gossip, there was no getting round the fact that she
was going to be living off this man's charity for some time
to come. It said a lot for his character that he was prepared
to do what he was doing. From living alone to having two
females he scarcely knew in his home would be no minor
disruption. The very least she could do by way of return
was to make life as easy as possible for him.

What little she knew about Barbados had been gleaned
from television holiday programmes, but it certainly looked
a beautiful place. She felt a sudden anticipatory ripple at
the thought of seeing it in the flesh, so to speak. It would
be the first time either she or Samantha had even been on
a plane, much less crossed the Atlantic!

With a trip into town in the offing, she went back up to
her room after they finished breakfast and exchanged jeans
and shirt for the grey skirt and jacket that was the one really
smart outfit she possessed. She even managed to find a pair
of unladdered tights. With her hair hanging loose about her
shoulders, she still looked less than her age, she acknowledged disconsolately, studying herself in the dressing table
mirror.

On impulse, she rooted in the drawer to find an elasti-
cated hair-binder, fastening the heavy length back into her
nape. Not a vast improvement, she had to admit, but the
best she could do for the moment.

Having changed his own clothing for the trousers and

cord jacket in which he had arrived, the white T-shirt replaced by a creamy-beige one bearing the same up-market logo, Nick was waiting in the living room.

'Amazing what a pair of high heels and a touch of lipstick can do,' he commented, looking her over.

'I'd no more go into town in jeans than you obviously would,' Erin responded swiftly, sensing derision. 'I thought I heard Sam come down.'

'She did. Several minutes ago. She's waiting in the car.'

'We never take the car into town,' she protested.

'*You* won't be doing now,' he returned. 'I will.'

Erin bit back the smart retort. If anyone owned the car, it was the bank, she supposed—or they would very shortly. 'Be it on your own head,' she said instead. 'The traffic will be murder!'

It was, though it didn't appear to bother him. He even managed to find a spare parking meter within easy walking distance of the Passport Office. Before presenting themselves, they obtained the necessary photographs via one of the machines, finishing up, as Samantha was moved to observe, looking like a couple of escapees from a lunatic asylum. Par for the course, according to Nick.

It was gone noon by the time they had the paperwork finished and the passports issued. With little food in the house at present, Erin was relieved when Nick suggested they had lunch here in town. It might be necessary to seek a sub in order to get in enough to see them over the weekend anyway, but she would cross that bridge if and when she came to it, she told herself. Right now, she intended enjoying being waited on for once.

Given the option, Samantha would have opted for the nearest burger bar, though she settled with reasonably good grace for the Italian restaurant that was Nick's choice of venue. Erin relished every mouthful of the chicken in red wine sauce she chose from an extensive menu, following it with a chocolate concoction that was nectar from heaven.

'I couldn't eat another crumb,' she admitted when Nick asked if she would like anything else. 'That was absolutely wonderful!'

He eyed her shrewdly. 'How long is it since you last ate out?'

'I can't remember,' she claimed, unwilling to go down that road.

'Dad didn't believe in it,' chimed in Samantha. '"Why pay somebody else to do what can be done at far less cost at home?" he always used to say. He used to go to restaurants himself, though.'

'With clients,' Erin corrected. 'Legitimate business expenses.'

'I don't think all of them could have been. I heard him telling somebody on the phone that the Inland Revenue was investigating him.'

'Not something you need worry about anyway,' Nick observed before Erin could make any further comment. 'Coffee?'

'I'll have a brandy,' said Samantha, responding to her uncle's glance with innocent eyes. 'That woman over there just ordered one.'

'When you're her age you can do the same,' he said.

The guilelessness increased. 'How do you know how old she is?'

'Call it an educated guess.'

'Stop playing silly games, Sam,' instructed Erin, wondering how long it would take for her sister's brand of humour to turn tolerance into irascibility. 'Do you want coffee or not?'

The younger girl pulled a face, drawing a shrug from Nick.

'I'll take that as a negative.'

They left the restaurant at two, but not, as Erin had anticipated, to go straight back to the house. He had a call of his own to pay first, Nick advised in the car.

Once again, he managed to find a parking place on a side street close by where he wanted to be. The luck of the devil, thought Erin, a little unfairly considering he'd been anything but to the pair of them so far.

'We'll wait here for you,' she said when he opened the door to get out. 'Assuming it isn't going to take long, that is?'

'I shouldn't think so,' he returned. 'The gallery's just round the corner there.'

Her interest perked up immediately. 'They have some of your stuff?'

'One or two, yes.'

'May we come with you?' she asked tentatively.

There was a slight hesitation before he nodded. 'No reason why not, I suppose.'

Its two windows draped in lemon silk and bearing just one easel-supported landscape in each, the gallery looked as exclusive as the area suggested. It was more spacious than it had appeared from outside, its subtly-lit depths partitioned into different areas. Apart from one wealthy-looking couple studying a work Erin couldn't see from this angle, they appeared to be the only callers.

The middle-aged man with long blond hair tied back in a ponytail who emerged from behind a curtain off to one side was something of a shock. Wearing a velvet suit in a brilliant burgundy, with silk ruffles at both neck and sleeve-ends, he looked more nineteenth than twentieth century. White teeth showed in a sparkling smile as he viewed the newcomers.

'Nicholas, *darling*, what a *wonderful* surprise!' he exclaimed extravagantly. 'Why didn't you let me know you were in town?'

'An unexpected visit.' Grinning, Nick held up a hand as the other advanced. 'Try kissing me, and I'll floor you!'

The smile turned into a pout, accompanied by an exaggerated sigh, fingers splayed over heart. 'Oh, the brute!'

'Aren't I always?' Nick glanced at the two girls. 'Meet Miles Penhalligen. My nieces, Erin and Samantha.'

Miles shook the hands both girls extended in turn, his clasp unexpectedly firm. 'There isn't much of *you* there,' he remarked, looking from one to the other. 'Far too pretty!'

'We both take after our mother,' Erin supplied. 'It's only Sam who's related anyway. We had different fathers.'

'Had?' Miles looked swiftly back to Nick.

'My brother died,' the other confirmed. 'How are things going?'

Miles took the hint, becoming suddenly businesslike. 'Gone. Your stuff is snapped up as soon as it's put on display. A real investment, considering the price one fetched at auction the other day. We might give some thought to upping the ante.'

'Does this mean we don't get to see any of your paintings after all?' asked Samantha.

'Not here and now,' her uncle confirmed.

'You can come and see the portrait he did of me and Rummy,' offered Miles, flicking a fastidious finger at a speck of fluff on his lapel. 'Not his best work, I'm afraid—he quite failed to capture Rummy's spirit—but better than nothing, I suppose.'

'That cat of yours doesn't *have* any spirit worth talking about,' Nick retorted, and drew an indignant look.

'He's aloof with you because he recognises your lack of empathy, darling. Do you like cats?' he asked the girls.

'Apart from the odd stray, I'm afraid we've never had much to do with them,' answered Erin, fighting to stay serious. 'But I'm sure we'd both love to meet Rummy.'

'And so you shall, if you can get this insensitive soul to bring you to my home.'

'It's doubtful if there's going to be time,' said the latter. 'We're leaving Monday.'

Miles looked intrigued. 'All three of you?'

'That's right.' Nick's tone was bland, his expression giving nothing away.

'Nicholas Carson bringing home a pair of lovely young nieces nobody knows about. That's really going to set the island buzzing! I'd give a whole lot to be a fly on the wall when the news hits the fan in certain quarters!' Miles broke off with a theatrical sigh as a man further down the gallery signalled for attention. 'Duty calls, I'm afraid, chickens. I'm all on my ownsome today.'

He kissed both girls continental-style, on both cheeks, contenting himself with a touch of lips to fingertips in Nick's direction. Samantha gave way to the giggles as they left the gallery.

'He's priceless!' she exclaimed. 'An absolute hoot!'

'He's also one of the most astute art dealers in London,' Nick advised drily, 'so don't let that act of his fool you. It amuses him to camp it up.'

Erin had guessed as much. Nick's whole attitude had suggested it. She stole a glance at the hard-boned face, wondering just which quarters Miles had been referring to with that 'fly on the wall' remark. Instinct suggested a woman.

The strength of her reaction to the idea of his being involved with someone shocked her. It was ridiculous to have any such feelings about a man not just fifteen years older than her but Sam's uncle to boot! She concentrated on the paving stones under her feet as if her life depended on not stepping on any lines.

Nick not only insisted on accompanying her into the supermarket on the way home, but paying the bill too.

'Something you're going to have to accept for the time being,' he observed on the way back to the car, when she made some only semi-joking remark about feeling like Orphan Annie. 'You don't have money, I do—ergo, I pay. It was my brother who got you into this fix in the first place.'

They had left Samantha listening to the radio in the car. Erin took a chance on asking the question she had been wanting to ask since his arrival. 'Did he try contacting you at all during the last few months?'

The lean features tautened a fraction. 'Yes,' he admitted. 'And, yes, I refused to help him out.'

'Which you feel guilty enough over to make amends by taking the two of us on,' Erin murmured, and received a cool hard glance.

'Don't try psychoanalysing me. I feel no guilt whatsoever where David's concerned.'

Erin didn't believe him. If he was as hard as he was making out, he wouldn't be doing what he was doing. She wished suddenly and fervently that she was older—able to meet him on level footing. He treated her like a child because to him that was all she was, but he didn't make her feel like a child.

'You've been absolute ages!' Samantha complained when they got to the car. 'We only needed enough to last over the weekend!'

'We don't know for sure yet that we'll be going on Monday,' Erin pointed out mildly, getting into the rear seat.

'Yes, we do.' Having stowed the bags in the boot, Nick slid behind the wheel. 'I booked the flight this morning, while I was waiting for you to get ready. Ten-twenty from Heathrow. We'll spend Sunday night at the Hilton to save any rush.'

Erin left it to Samantha to make the appropriate noises,

telling herself she wasn't yet fully committed; reservations could always be cancelled.

But she knew deep down that it was beyond her to pull out now.

CHAPTER THREE

APART from odd wisps of cloud drifting across from time to time, there was nothing to mar the view straight down to a sea that looked flat calm from this height, the occasional ships like toys in a bathtub.

Samantha had long ago grown bored with looking at it, and been only too happy to exchange seats. Flying, she had declared with lofty disdain, was no big deal.

It certainly was for her, Erin reflected, nose pressed against the glass; more especially flying first class. From the moment of reaching the airport this morning they had been treated like Royalty, with drinks and snacks served in the VIP lounge, and an escort to take them to the plane.

Nick had taken it all in his stride, of course, obviously well accustomed to treading the red carpet. Erin had begun to wonder just how affluent he really was. Artists she had read about seemed to have spent much of their lives struggling to keep body and soul together.

He was seated right behind her; if she turned her head just a fraction she could catch a glimpse of him from the corner of her eye. The book he had been reading appeared to have been laid aside in favour of a sketchpad.

Supple and sensitive, those long-fingered hands were the only part of him that fitted the artistic image. The rest was pure masculinity. All through dinner at the hotel last night she had been aware of the interest he was drawing from other women in the restaurant—especially one seated at the adjoining table. If he'd noted it himself—which he could hardly fail to have done—he'd paid no heed. No doubt he was well accustomed to that kind of attention too.

As if in direct response to that assessment, one of the stewardesses paused by his seat to ask if there was anything she could get him, following the query with a gratified-sounding exclamation.

'Would you like it?' asked Nick.

'I'd love it!' she sparkled. 'I've never had a portrait done before.'

He laughed. 'Hardly a portrait.'

'As good as, to me,' came the response. 'Would you sign it for me?'

'Sure.' There was a brief pause, followed by the sound of a page being torn from the pad. 'Here you are.'

'I'll treasure this,' the recipient assured him. 'My very own Nicholas Carson!'

'Don't you wish!' murmured Samantha. She looked up with bland expression as the stewardess moved on to direct the same question at the pair of them. 'Can we have a look?'

An extremely attractive brunette in her late twenties, the woman smiled and offered the sketch for appraisal. It was, Erin acknowledged, an excellent likeness.

'Nice,' Samantha commented, handing it back.

'Isn't it!' the other agreed, directing another smile at the man seated behind. 'It's very flattering to be considered worth the trouble.'

'No trouble,' Nick assured her easily. 'Bone structure like yours is an artist's dream!'

If the woman's chest swelled any further, her boobs were going to burst her blouse buttons, thought Erin uncharitably. Talk about laying it on with a trowel!

Never backward in coming forward, Samantha turned to direct a grin between the seats at her uncle as the stewardess moved on. 'Great chat-up line!'

'You're too young for such cynicism,' came the equable response. 'She does have good bone structure.'

'So do I,' claimed Samantha promptly, 'but you haven't offered to sketch *me*.'

'Would you like me to?'

'I thought you'd never ask!'

'So come and sit back here where I can see you.' Nick was obviously amused.

She did so with alacrity, plumping into the empty seat at his side. 'Full-face or profile?'

'Whichever, so long as you keep reasonably still.'

'Profile, then,' she decided. 'I might start laughing if I'm looking at you.'

Listening, Erin doubted if she could ever bring herself to be as much at ease with him as her sister was. The physical thing aside, much of the problem still lay in the fact that while with Sam there was at least a blood factor, she had no claim on him whatsoever. Taking the costs already incurred on her account, she was in debt to him for more than she could ever hope to repay.

The sketch was completed at what seemed lightning speed, to be viewed with a critical eye by its subject.

'You've made me look like a kid!' she complained.

'You *are* a kid,' Nick returned drily. 'Do you want it, or shall I tear it up?'

'I'll take it,' she condescended. 'How about doing one of Erin now?'

'Another time,' he said, before Erin could frame a rejection. 'I'd like to get back to my book.'

Sam took the hint, returning to her seat to toss the sketch into Erin's lap with a deprecatory air. Regardless of what her sister might think, Nick had captured the youthfully pretty face to perfection in Erin's estimation. She hoped he didn't think she was disappointed by his refusal to comply with Sam's suggestion. Having herself portrayed on paper was the *last* thing on her mind.

From the first glimpse of the green-clad jewel of an island, fringed by beaches of pure white sand, she was too much in thrall to think about anything else. The sun was still high in the clear blue sky when they landed, the sheer quality of light a revelation in itself.

Nick was greeted by airport staff with smiling familiarity, the speculation regarding her and Samantha obvious. On an island the size of this one, the news would spread like wildfire, Erin imagined. What might be made of it was something else.

They took a taxi from the airport, disappointing Samantha who had been expecting some fancy limousine to be waiting for them.

'The inland roads aren't suited to limos,' said Nick, when she asked if he had one. 'I use a Jeep as a general runabout myself, but there's a Mercedes 190 in the garage. If you drive, I can get you put on the insurance,' he added to Erin.

'Yes, I do, but I'll be perfectly happy using the bus when I need to go anywhere,' she assured him swiftly. 'I imagine there's a service?'

'It would be a pretty fair walk from the house to the nearest pickup point. If it's independence you're after, you could always learn to ride a moped.'

Hardly a hardship in this climate, Erin conceded, looking out on gently undulating landscape and rioting colour, though buying such a machine was a long way from being a viable proposition. Not that she found the thought of walking to a bus stop off-putting.

'It's all so utterly beautiful!' she exclaimed, transport problems thrust aside. 'I've never seen so many different flowers!'

'You'll soon get used to it.' Nick sounded tolerant. 'A month, and you'll be taking it all for granted.'

'Never!' She could say that with certainty. She turned back to look at him, too euphoric to be reticent. 'I can imagine how different it's going to be for you, having the

two of us around, but I'll do everything I can to keep things
running smoothly. Anything at all I can do for you, you
only have to ask.'

The smile was more than a touch ironical. 'I'll bear it in
mind.'

Seated, at her own request, up front beside the driver,
Samantha was chatting away as though she had known the
man for years. There was one who was going to have no
trouble at all adjusting to her new life, reflected Erin.
Hopefully, her wayward streak wouldn't surface too often.

Its faded pink walls covered in creeper threaded through
with bougainvillaea, lower reaches shaded by wide white-
railed verandas, the house they eventually reached via a
curving driveway edged with flamboyant was a delight to
the eye. A place like this must cost the earth! thought Erin
dazedly. She was forced to revise her estimate of their ben-
efactor's possible worth once again as she viewed smoothly
manicured emerald-green lawns edged by majestic Royal
Palms, the eye-dazzling profusion of blooms and shrubs.
Maintenance of the grounds alone had to be a full-time job!

'You must be absolutely rolling in it!' exclaimed
Samantha enthusiastically, echoing her own thoughts. 'Is
there a swimming pool too?'

'Out back,' Nick acknowledged. 'It was being cleaned
when I left, so it might not be useable yet.'

'I'll go take a look!' she said, and headed off along the
path leading round the side of the house.

Erin eyed Nick uncomfortably, thankful that the taxi
driver wasn't still around to witness her sister's appalling
lack of manners. 'Sorry about that.'

'About what?' he asked.

'The comment Sam made. It was totally out of order!'

'On the premise that it's vulgar to refer to money?' He
lifted his shoulders. 'I'd hardly be living here if I were a
pauper.'

'I realise that. It's just—' She broke off, spreading her hands in a wry little gesture. 'I'm feeling a bit overwhelmed by it all, I suppose.'

Nick made no reply, studying the smooth young face upturned to his with an unreadable expression in his eyes. Looking back at him, Erin felt the familiar tingle run down her spine, and found it hard to maintain a steady gaze. Not only would it be downright embarrassing to have him guess the effect he had on her, but possibly disastrous, in the sense that he might consider the situation untenable. It was only a temporary attraction anyway. It *had* to be.

The screened double doors at the rear of the veranda were flung back suddenly to frame an ample figure in a bright orange dress, her face split almost from ear to ear by a sparkling white smile.

'Mr Nick! I thought that was a car I heard!'

'Hallo, Bella,' he said. 'My housekeeper,' he added, for Erin's benefit. 'The finest on the island!'

'None of that soft talk!' she chided, exchanging the smile for a frown as she viewed the newcomer. 'Why didn't you let me know you were coming home—and bringin' a visitor too!'

'Two visitors,' he corrected imperturbably. 'The other one went to take a look at the pool. This is Miss Grainger.'

'Erin,' said the latter, managing a smile of her own. 'Nice to meet you, Bella. I'm sorry to land on you unexpectedly.'

'What's done's done,' came the unmollified response. 'I'll need to get some rooms ready.'

'Let me help,' Erin offered, and received an affronted shake of the head.

'I don't need no help! And Joshua will do that,' she scolded her employer as he bent to lift the two suitcases. 'You just come and sit while I fix you some tea.'

'I may as well bring these in with me now,' said Nick

mildly. 'Josh can take them up. Make that tea for two,' he added, ushering Erin ahead of him through the doorway as the housekeeper shifted her not inconsiderable bulk to make room. 'I'll have a whisky.'

'It's too early to be drinkin' that stuff!' declared Bella.

'Probably.' Nick hadn't altered his tone, but the message apparently got through all the same, lifting the housekeeper's shoulders in a resigned shrug.

'Some folk just don't listen to reason.'

She went off, grumbling under her breath, her movements surprisingly light for someone her weight. Dropping the suitcases to the coolly tiled floor of the spacious entrance hall, Nick caught Erin's eye and grinned briefly.

'You'll need to stand up for yourself with Bella. She considers it her duty to keep everybody on the straight and narrow.'

'Obviously she doesn't have too much success with you,' Erin returned, still trying to come to terms with it all.

'I'm past redemption.' He indicated an archway off to the right. 'Let's go and find your sister.'

The room into which he took her was sumptuous by any standards—a vast expanse of pale cream carpet, warm woodwork and fresh tropical colour. Glass doors gave onto the rear veranda, with a view out over more landscaped gardens containing a free-form pool complete with a central island.

Turning from her contemplation of the latter, Samantha waved a cheery hand as she spotted them through the glass. Nick crossed to open one of the doors, admitting a subtle fragrance.

'Come on in,' he invited.

She obeyed, stepping across the threshold to view the room appreciatively. 'Some place!' she commented. 'Must have cost you a bomb!'

'Home to you for the next few years at least,' her uncle advised, cutting across Erin's remonstrance.

'I feel completely at home already,' she returned chirpily. 'I always knew I was destined for the high life!'

Nick gave a short laugh. 'You won't find things so very different once you're acclimatised. Schools tend to be much the same wherever you are.'

She pulled a face. 'You would have to remind me! Still—' on a cheerier note '—I'll hardly be going right away, will I?'

'Depends how soon it can be arranged,' he said. 'I'll get onto it first thing in the morning.'

The rattle of crockery heralded the approach of Bella, pushing a loaded trolley. She regarded Samantha with even greater disconcertion.

'You didn't say nothin' about no child,' she accused. 'Come to it, you haven't said nothin' about anythin'!'

'An omission about to be corrected,' returned the master of the house. 'This is my brother's daughter, Samantha. Erin is her half-sister. They're going to be living here.'

'You mean all the time?'

'That's the idea.'

The woman looked from one to the other girl as if she could hardly believe what she was hearing. 'You plannin' on adoptin' them both?'

'I'm a little past adoption age,' Erin cut in hastily. 'We'll do our best not to cause you any extra work, Bella.'

'I'll even make my own bed every morning,' offered Samantha magnanimously. 'You won't know we're here!'

'I already know you're here.' Bella was unamused. 'You best get your tea while it's still hot.'

'I'll be mother, shall I?' said Samantha brightly as the housekeeper went off.

Nick gave her a quelling look. '*You* can sit down and behave yourself. Erin can do the honours.'

He left them to it, crossing to a cedarwood cabinet to pour himself the promised whisky. There were three cups and saucers on the trolley, Erin noted; obviously Bella wasn't one to accept defeat easily. Her reaction to the news that she and Samantha were to be permanent fixtures was hardly to be wondered at. Nick could surely have given some kind of warning via the phone rather than simply dropping them on her out of the blue this way!

He came back to take a seat opposite her own, lifting one leg casually across the other.

'I need this,' he said, catching Erin's eye as he raised the heavy glass to his lips. 'It's been quite a week!'

'For all of us,' she returned meaningfully, and saw his lips slant.

'Point taken. Maybe you'd like something stronger yourself?'

She shook her head. 'The tea will do me fine, thanks.'

'I wouldn't mind something stronger,' declared Samantha, already halfway through a succulent fruit tart. 'I was never very keen on tea anyway.'

'Just drink it,' Erin said shortly, tolerance running out. 'Think yourself lucky to be here at all!'

The blue eyes so like her own flashed in swift resentment. 'I've more right than you, at any rate!'

'Cut that out!' Nick hadn't altered his position, but the sudden snap in his voice left no room for misunderstanding. 'You apologise to your sister—now!'

'She didn't…' Erin began, voice petering out in face of the glance he briefly turned her way.

Looking a little shell-shocked, Samantha did as she was told, subsiding into aggrieved silence. Erin wanted to tell her it was okay, that she knew she hadn't really meant what she'd said. Nick had jumped so hard and fast, stunning them both with the swift metamorphosis.

He drained the glass and put it down on the lamp table

by his elbow, expression still verging on the flinty. 'You owe Erin some respect,' he said. 'She sacrificed a lot to be dogsbody for you and your father this last few years.'

'That was hardly Sam's fault,' Erin protested. 'And a little housework and cooking hardly merits the term "dogsbody"!'

Nick gave her an exasperated look. 'There's a damn sight more than that to running a household, and well you know it! I saw the way Sam here took it for granted that it was *your* place to see to everything the last few days, so don't try making out you had help from any quarter.'

'Sam had school, and Dad had business affairs to deal with,' she said.

'You should have been in school yourself.' He shook his head as she started to form a response. 'You don't owe my brother any loyalty. Judging from the amount of luggage you've brought between you, I'd say he kept a pretty tight grasp on the purse strings all round.'

'We just brought what we thought we were going to need,' Erin defended. 'There didn't seem much point in packing winter things for this climate.'

'We don't have all that many summer clothes either,' Samantha chimed in, recovering her spirits.

'No problem,' said her uncle. 'There are plenty of good boutiques in Bridgetown.'

'Charging plenty too, I'd imagine.' Erin gave him back look for look. 'You must do as you see fit where Sam's concerned, of course, but I can manage well enough with what I already have.'

Nick lifted an eyebrow. 'That depends on what you *do* have. I've a position to keep up in this community.'

'I'm hardly going to be going places where it matters what I'm wearing.'

'That pride of yours could become wearing.' He sounded

as if that time might already have come. 'Will you get it through your head that you're not here as a charity case?'

'I'm certainly not here for the reasons you led me to believe,' she returned shortly. 'With a resident house-keeper, you're already safeguarded against defamatory gossip.'

He made an impatient movement. 'I don't give a damn about "defamatory gossip"! You're here because Sam needs you.'

'Yes, I do!' The younger girl both looked and sounded eager to convince. 'I didn't mean what I said just now. You know I didn't! I'd be lost without you.'

Erin doubted it. Not in present surroundings. 'I'm sorry,' she said hollowly. 'I must appear very ungrateful.'

'I don't want your gratitude.' Nick's tone was curt. 'Malvern is as much home to you as it is to Samantha, so stop acting the poor relation!'

Erin's chin lifted, a spark lighting her eyes. 'I'm not *acting* anything! If I'd known how you lived—'

'Just what kind of lifestyle did you imagine I lived?'

'One where I could at least make myself useful. You never mentioned staff.'

'It didn't occur to me to mention them. As to making yourself useful, I've a mountain of paperwork that could do with sorting. I don't want to hear another word on the subject,' he added as she once more made to speak.

There was nothing much else she *could* say, Erin concluded heavily. With little or no means of her own to fall back on, she was stuck with the situation. Some people might call her a fool for carping about it.

Bella returned to say that their rooms were ready. Accompanying her up the lovely balustraded staircase, Erin attempted to engage her in light conversation, giving up when her overtures elicited no more than monosyllabic replies. She didn't blame the woman for her attitude. Having

two permanent additions to the household thrust upon her
without warning was reason enough for grievance.

Judging from the initial reaction, any offer to help around
the house was obviously going to be taken as a dire insult,
but that didn't mean she had to accept being waited on hand
and foot. There must be things she could do that wouldn't
get up Bella's nose. All it needed was a little tact and diplomacy.

Both bedrooms were at the rear of the house, overlooking
the pool and gardens and allowing a distant glimpse of the
sea through the far trees. Each had its own beautifully ap-
pointed bathroom and sitting area, with French doors giving
onto an upper balcony running the whole length of the
house.

'It's really cool!' Samantha proclaimed. 'Just imagine
living here all the time!'

Expression dour, Bella left them to it, muttering beneath
her breath as she went. Erin sat down on the edge of the
double bed, feeling as limp as a wrung-out wet rag. Her
sister eyed her curiously.

'You really didn't take what I said a bit back seriously,
did you?' she asked.

Erin forced a smile. 'Of course not. It was my fault for
coming the big sister the way I did. I'm just finding it a bit
hard to take in, that's all.'

'I'm not,' claimed the younger girl. 'It's *exactly* what *I*
expected!' She performed an exuberant twirl, ponytail
swinging, eyes sparkling like twin sapphires. 'I'm going to
love every minute!'

A very large proportion of which would be spent in
school, it was on the tip of Erin's tongue to remind her,
but she held it back. It could be several days—even a week
or more—before Nick managed to get her enrolled in one.
Why burst the bubble now?

'We'd better unpack,' she said instead. 'Not that we're

either of us going to fill more than a fraction of those.' She glanced in the direction of the walk-in closet on the far side of the room.

Samantha gave a dismissive shrug. 'I'll be having lots of new things anyway. You should too. You heard what Nick said about keeping up appearances.'

'I'm sure he spends sleepless nights worrying about it.' Erin hesitated before adding cautiously, 'Try not to go overboard, Sam. There has to be a limit.'

'I don't see why. He's hardly short of a dollar or two, as Dad used to say.' Viewing her sister's expression, Samantha laughed. 'Stop being so stuffy, Rin! He's our uncle, after all.'

'*Your* uncle, not mine,' Erin replied firmly. 'I dare say he'll set his own limits anyway.'

For all the notice taken, she might as well have held her breath. Samantha was too well ensconced on cloud nine to be fetched down by words. 'I'm going to find a cossie and have a swim before anything else,' she announced. 'The pool awaits!'

It was going to be up to Nick himself to establish some ground rules, thought Erin resignedly as the door closed in her sister's wake. He had made something of a start earlier, but Sam had soon bounced back. He hadn't even begun to experience the worst.

Unpacking her one suitcase and travel bag took no more than fifteen minutes. As anticipated, her things looked lost in the huge closet. She had a long, slow shower, unable to avoid her image in the mirrored walls as she towelled herself down. Her breasts were so small, she thought disconsolately. No man was ever going to be turned on by the sight of them.

She left it there, unwilling to acknowledge that the one man she might want to turn on was unlikely to be stirred by anything *she* could offer.

Back in the bedroom, she donned clean underwear and got into a blue cotton tunic that owed its length more to the fact that she had grown since acquiring it than any fashion statement. Darkness had already fallen, stirring the crickets to vibrant life. Erin went out onto the balcony, leaning on the rail to draw in great breaths of the fragrant night air as she looked at a sky strewn with stars twice as big and bright as back home.

Despite everything, she couldn't help being glad she was here. Who wouldn't prefer to live in this lovely place? There had to be some kind of work she could get. Bridgetown sounded the right place to start looking. Tomorrow, she reminded herself ironically, was a whole new day.

Supper was served out on the veranda by a cheerful West Indian whom Nick introduced as Bella's husband, Joshua Parish. They had their quarters in a converted stable block some short distance from the main house, he advised, with a sardonic glance in Erin's direction, so the three of them would have the house to themselves at night.

'What made you buy a place this size in the first place?' Erin queried, refusing to react to the taunt.

Broad shoulders lifted. 'I like space. Anyway, you never know when people might drop in.'

'Do you have lots of visitors?' asked Samantha.

'Lots, no. Some, yes.'

'We'll make sure not to get in the way when they do come,' said Erin, and received another mocking glance.

'I'm sure you will.'

Samantha spooned up the last of her flamed banana with a sigh of pure bliss. 'Scrumptious! I love it here!'

You haven't been here five minutes, Erin wanted to say, but she held her tongue, conscious of the grey eyes still resting on her. Wearing a casual white shirt and tan chinos, dark hair still slightly damp from the shower, he had set her heart racing again the moment she clapped eyes on him. It was no use reminding herself about the age gap—it made absolutely no difference to her responses. Where Nick Carson was concerned, her body had a will of its own.

'How soon can we make that trip into Bridgetown?' Samantha asked next, thoughts turning from inner to outer gratification. She smiled the sweet smile that deceived so many people into believing her thoroughly angelic. 'It's going to be wonderful to have new things! This—' casting a wry downward glance at the dress she had on '—barely fits me any more—and the others are even worse!'

'I guess we'd better make it tomorrow, then,' said Nick. 'I've business of my own to attend to, so it's going to be up to you to kit her out with whatever she needs,' he added to Erin. 'Naturally you'll be provided with the where-withal.' He paused, lip tilting at the corner as he viewed her expression. 'Don't worry, I'm not about to suggest you take advantage yourself.'

'Good,' she responded, rallying her forces. 'If it's going to be down to me, I'll need a set figure to work with.'

'All you'll need is my card as authority to charge.'

Erin gave up. It was hardly her place to try dictating how much—or little—he should spend on his own niece. That Samantha herself would take full advantage of an open-ended arrangement was without a doubt. It would serve him right if she ran up some astronomical bill.

The blue tunic seemed to be revealing a great deal too much bare leg when she rose from the table in response to Nick's suggestion that they adjourn to the wickerwork chairs grouped about a low table further along the veranda for coffee. She was conscious of him looking at her—sensed the derisive smile. So what? she thought defiantly. Her legs were probably her best feature anyway.

Both low and deep, the chairs were designed for relax-ation rather than decorum. Erin stopped even trying to keep her lower thighs covered, concentrating on the sounds and scents and wonderful velvety warmth of the Caribbean night instead. Moths of all shapes and sizes fluttered about the lights, but there appeared to be no biting insects around. One of the few places in the world devoid of snakes of any kind, she had read somewhere. That had to be a plus in itself.

'Where do you have your studio?' she heard herself asking.

'It's behind the old mill. I like to be right away from it all when I'm working.' Leaning back in his seat, legs stretched, hands clasped comfortably behind his head, Nick both looked and sounded relaxed. 'Did you ever do any painting yourself?'

'Only in school.'

'Were you any good?'

'Brilliant!' interposed Samantha before Erin could answer. 'Everybody said so!'

Erin gave a deprecatory little laugh. 'Stop exaggerating, Sam!'

'Who's exaggerating?' she said. 'You were set on going to art college until Dad blackmailed you into taking over Mum's job. Not that she ever did all that much to start with.'

'Don't talk about her like that!' Erin remonstrated sharply. 'Your father either. Blackmail's a ridiculous word to use!'

Samantha stuck out a stubborn lip. 'No, it isn't. He said you owed it to him for giving you a home in the first place, *and* letting you stay after Mum went off. I heard him!'

'Did he?' Nick's jaw had tautened. 'Don't flannel me,' he admonished as Erin hesitated. 'This is *my* brother we're talking about.'

'He was experiencing some financial difficulties even

back then,' she defended. 'I was happy to help any way I could.'

'Why make excuses for him? He acted deplorably.'

'No worse than you refusing to help him out,' she flashed, instantly regretting the hasty rejoinder as she saw the grey eyes harden.

'I've told you before, that's my affair!'

'I know.' She spread her hands in a contrite little gesture. 'I've no right to make any judgements. Especially when...'

'Especially when you owe *me* so much,' he finished drily as she let the words trail away. 'It goes against the grain to be beholden to anyone, doesn't it?'

'When I've no way of paying back, yes.' She was doing her best to stay on even keel. 'As I'm obviously not going to be allowed to do anything much around the house, I aim to find a job.'

'Offering what kind of experience?'

'I can cook, and clean.'

'So can hundreds of others. As an alien, you'd only be allowed to take a job no resident could be found to fill, which limits the choice even further.'

'It looks like you'll have to settle for being a kept woman after all, Rin,' observed Samantha blandly.

Face warming, Erin saw Nick's lips twitch. At that precise moment, she could cheerfully have wrung her sister's neck.

'I don't think it need come to quite that,' he said. 'As I mentioned earlier, there's a whole lot of paperwork needs sorting out for starters.'

She hesitated. 'I wouldn't want to know your affairs.'

'You wouldn't glean all that much if you did.' Nick was beginning to sound a mite exasperated again. 'Do you want the job or don't you?'

Anything, Erin decided, was better than just sitting back

and accepting a life of leisure at his expense. 'I want it,' she said. 'Along with anything else you can find me to do.'

'I'll give the matter some serious thought.'

She said no more, conscious of the underlying impatience in his tone. She could to a certain extent understand his attitude. What she couldn't do was allow it to influence her own attitude. Pride was all she had.

Samantha gave a sudden yawn. 'I can't possibly be tired yet!' she complained. 'It's not even ten o'clock!'

'Almost two in the morning by your body clock,' Nick reminded her. 'Why don't you go on up? You'll need to be fresh and bright for all this shopping tomorrow.'

The thought alone was enough to convince her. Erin made a move to get to her feet along with the younger girl, subsiding again with some reluctance in answer to Nick's gesture. The last thing she wanted right now was to be alone with him.

CHAPTER FOUR

IF SAMANTHA had seen the gesture, she made no comment, taking herself off with a cheery, 'Night, all!'

Silence reigned for several moments after her departure. Erin was the first to break it. 'You wanted to say something?'

Nick gave an easy shrug. 'I just thought it would be nice for the grown-ups to have half an hour on their own.'

'Another promotion?' she asked a little more tartly than intended.

'It wasn't meant sarcastically,' he returned on a mild note. 'Just as a matter of interest, when do you get to be twenty?'

Erin modulated her tone. 'October.'

'Now there's a coincidence! Same month as me. We'll have to plan a double celebration.'

'It's a long time yet,' she said.

'You're thinking you might not even be here still by then?'

'I...suppose.'

He made no immediate reply, studying her reflectively. Erin put up an automatic hand to rake the heavy fall of fair hair back from her forehead, serving to lift the tunic hem even further up her thigh. She saw the grey eyes drop the length of her body to linger for an interminable moment on the silky expanse of bare flesh, and was hard put to it to stop herself from showing discomposure.

'I'd like you to sit for me some time,' he said unexpectedly, throwing her into even more confusion.

'Why?' she got out.

The mobile left eyebrow lifted. 'I don't normally need to give a reason.'

Erin could imagine. Most people would be only too flattered by the interest. 'Do you specialise in portraits?' she asked.

'No. I paint whatever or whoever I'm moved to paint.'

'Like the airline stewardess?'

A hint of a smile flickered across his lips. 'Like the airline stewardess.'

'You weren't interested in drawing me on the plane,' she reminded him.

'You call for rather more care and attention than I'd put into any quick sketch,' he said. 'I knew it the first time I saw you standing there, with your back to the door, all legs and eyes like a wary young gazelle. That's the way I want to paint you.'

'In a nightdress?'

The smile came again. 'What did you think I might want—a nude study?'

'Of course not,' she denied hastily. 'I hardly have the...attributes.'

'You reckon large breasts are an essential factor? Not so, I can assure you.'

'I'll bet!' she slung back, losing what little was left of her composure. Eyes brilliant, spots of colour burning high on her cheekbones, she got to her feet. 'I'm going to bed.'

Nick didn't stir, amusement replaced by an expression much harder to define. 'If you won't sit for me by choice, you can do it as part of the "anything I can find" you asked for. A fairly painless price to pay, wouldn't you say?'

Erin made her escape with a muttered goodnight, still unable to convince herself that he wasn't simply making fun of her. A gazelle indeed!

She prepared for bed quickly, donning one of the cotton nightdresses she always wore. Like the walls, the bathroom door was fully mirrored. Leaving the room, she was faced with a view that had, she realised, to be very similar to the one she must have presented the night Nick arrived. It was certainly true that she was showing a great deal of long, slender leg, but her eyes looked ordinary enough—as did the rest of her.

On impulse, she lifted both hands to cup the modest curves for a moment, testing the consistency. They were firm enough, but hardly a handful for her, much less...

This had to stop right here and now! she told herself forcibly. Nick's interest in her was purely artistic.

She slept fitfully, coming wide awake at six to a morning too glorious for despondency of any kind. Dressed in her usual uniform of jeans and practical cotton shirt, she crept downstairs to let herself out via the French doors from the living room, feeling the air like soft silk on her skin.

The sound of voices came faintly to her ears, although there was no one in sight. She headed away from the sound, rounding the far end of the pool to follow a path meandering through lush shrubbery. Colour danced before her eyes wherever she looked, ranging through delicate pinks and blues and yellows to the exotic red-orange of the flamboyant. Bougainvillaea spilled over old stone walls and arches.

Paradise must be like this, thought Erin whimsically, breaking off a small spray of frangipani to inhale the sweet, tantalising scent. Other matters aside, it was certainly going to be no hardship living here.

She emerged upon a grassy clearing backed by the creeper-covered remains of the old mill Nick had spoken of last night. Jutting out from the rear was a glass-roofed extension that could only be the studio.

About to turn and head back the way she had come, Erin hesitated. There was surely nothing wrong with just taking a look through the windows while no one was about?

The area within was far more spacious than it looked from outside. There were racks of canvasses stacked against the rear wall, protected by covers. An easel held yet another, also covered, the palette and other tools of trade on a nearby table suggesting a work not yet completed.

Finding the door unlocked when she tentatively tried it gave rise to further hesitation, but the temptation was too strong for her. Just a quick peep, she promised herself.

No quick peep was going to be enough, she realised at once on easing back a cover to reveal a stormy seascape so wonderfully executed that the towering waves seemed about to leap from the canvas and engulf her. She forgot about trespassing, forgot about everything over the following minutes, lost in admiration of a talent greater even than she had been led to expect.

It took movement from the doorway to jerk her out of it. Leaning against the doorjamb, thumbs hooked into the pockets of his jeans, Nick viewed her with enigmatic expression.

'How long have you been here?' he asked.

'Just a few minutes,' she said uncomfortably. 'I'm sorry. I know I shouldn't have come in, but the door was unlocked and I couldn't...I didn't—' She broke off, lifting her shoulders in a wry little shrug. 'I don't have any excuses.'

'You don't need any excuses,' he returned. 'I'm sure you can be trusted not to damage anything.' He paused, making no attempt to come further into the room. 'So what's the verdict?'

Erin looked at him suspiciously, but there was no telltale curl at the corner of the strong mouth. 'For what it's worth, I think they're exceptional,' she said.

This time his lip quite definitely did curl. 'You consider your opinion of no great importance?'

'I only meant I'm no art critic,' she parried.

'According to Samantha, you've a talent of your own.'

Erin forced a laugh. 'I wouldn't take anything Sam says too seriously. I can draw a bit, that's all.' She let the cover she was holding up fall back into place. 'Are all these going to be for sale?'

'Eventually, yes. They're due for shipping out the end of the month.'

'To Miles Penhalligen?'

He shook his head. 'To New York. You can help pack when the crates arrive. One more job to add to the list.'

'Still nowhere near enough.'

'A matter of opinion. Which brings us back to where we started.'

He straightened from the doorjamb in one lithe movement, bringing her heart into her throat as he came over to where she stood to take her by the shoulders and turn her further into the light.

'You've no idea how lovely you are, have you?' he said. He drew a fingertip down the side of her cheek, tracing the delicate line of her jaw with a featherlight touch that stimulated every nerve ending in her body. 'Wonderful bone structure!'

'Me and the stewardess both,' she managed with creditable flippancy, and saw his lips curve.

'With her it was something of a line, with you it's a fact. Sam has it too, although it hasn't fully emerged as yet. Your mother must have been a very beautiful woman.'

Erin steeled herself not to move as he ran both hands into her hair, to smooth it back from her face, eyes narrowed in concentrated assessment. Flattering that he found her worthy of his artistic interest at least, she thought wryly.

'It might have been better if she hadn't been,' she said, not a bit surprised to hear the unsteadiness in her voice.

'Because it drew men to her?'

'Like moths to a candle-flame, your brother used to say.' He had actually used a far cruder term, but she had no intention of repeating it. 'The man she ran away with was a business acquaintance of his.'

'That must have been tough on him.'

The expression in the grey eyes had altered subtly. She could feel the tremoring response spreading through her body, and knew he must feel it too. She wanted him to draw her closer, to know what it was like to be in his arms, his lips on hers, his hands caressing her—possessing her.

'I'm not the one to take you down that road,' Nick said softly, letting her go. 'Tempting proposition though it is.'

Erin drew in a mortified breath, the warmth rushing up under her skin. 'I don't know what you're talking about,' she said, attempting to infuse a genuine-sounding bewilderment.

The smile was brief. 'Yes, you do. It was coming from you in waves. Considering your lifestyle up to now, I'm probably the first male you've ever been in close enough contact with to light the spark. You'll soon get over it.'

'I'll take your word for it,' she said thickly, abandoning any further face-saving denials. 'I'm sorry to have embarrassed you.'

'You haven't.' There was a certain irony in his voice. 'We'd better get back to the house.'

He made no attempt to converse on the way, just strolled at her side as if nothing of any note had happened. She should be grateful, Erin supposed, that he had let her down so gently. Another man might have taken advantage of her girlish passions. A temptation, he had said; she wondered if he had really meant it or was simply pandering to her ego.

Either way, she had to stop thinking of him in any sense other than as Sam's uncle, she told herself bleakly. There was no future in anything else.

It was a surprise to find Sam already up and dressed when they got back to the house.

'I've been awake ages!' claimed the girl. 'I was going to have a swim, but I wasn't sure what time we'd be setting off for town?' The last directed at her uncle.

'I want to be in town by nine,' he said, 'so we'll be leaving eight-thirty.'

'Great!' she enthused, sobering to add plaintively, 'When's breakfast? I'm starving!'

As if in direct response to the question, Bella appeared round the corner of the veranda, pushing a loaded trolley.

'If it's late it's because you're early,' she berated, obviously having heard the remark. 'Breakfast is *always* eight o'clock.'

'Apart from when I ask for it earlier,' said Nick mildly. 'We'll be back for lunch the usual time.'

'That's somethin' I s'pose.' Not noticeably appeased, the housekeeper transferred the trolley contents to the already laid table, and departed, her head-up carriage only too indicative of her frame of mind.

'Why do you let her speak to you like that?' asked Samantha. 'She's only a servant.'

Grey eyes turned suddenly steely. 'Bella isn't *only* anything. You'll treat her with the respect she's due!'

'I don't think Sam meant—' Erin began.

'Yes, she did,' he cut in. 'And I'm not having it. Is that clear?'

'What about the respect *we're* due?' retorted his niece, sticking out the stubborn underlip. 'It isn't nice being made to feel like intruders.'

'She'll come round,' he said. 'She's just annoyed that I didn't consult her first.'

'Why didn't you, then?'

Erin held her breath, waiting for the explosion, letting it out again slowly when he failed to react the way his expression had indicated he might.

'An oversight, I have to admit.' He moved abruptly. 'Let's eat.'

Erin took her place at the table, feeling anything but happy. There was a limit as to how much Nick was going to be prepared to take from her sister, and she had very nearly reached it a moment ago. Between the two of them, he must be fed up to the back teeth already.

One thing he didn't do was indulge in displeased silences, keeping up a light conversation throughout the meal.

'Before I forget,' he said at one point, fishing out a small square card from a back pocket and sliding it across the table to where Erin sat, 'you'd better have this. I suppose I'd be wasting my breath suggesting you take advantage of it too?'

'Totally,' she confirmed, wondering even as she said it just what she was going to wear for this shopping trip. She had travelled in the grey suit, but it was far too warm for here. 'Not that I don't appreciate the offer,' she tagged on.

'Taken as read,' he said drily.

Completely recovered from any chastening effect, Samantha was overflowing with enthusiasm for the coming expedition. Erin wished she had just a fraction of her sister's ability to dismiss past discomfitures. The humiliation she had suffered earlier still burned within her, and would continue to do so for a long time to come. She felt so unutterably gauche.

She made her escape as soon as possible to go and riffle through the all too few garments in her closet, settling in the end on a multi-coloured skirt and a white blouse that had both come from a charity shop. Scarcely worn when she'd acquired them, her sandals were from the latter too. Even at charity shop prices, she had been unable to afford more than the occasional foray, but what she did have was at least of good quality.

Nick made no comment this time when he saw her. He had changed his own jeans and T-shirt for a pair of white trousers and a rust-coloured shirt open on the strong brown column of his throat, creating more havoc. She couldn't stop herself from feeling this way about him, Erin acknowledged dispiritedly. All she could do was learn to conceal it. Starting right now.

Bridgetown was bustling with traffic of both the motorised and pedestrianised kind. Nick parked the car close by the Careenage, where inter-island schooners unloaded cargoes of plantains, heading back along the wharf to Trafalgar Square with its picturesque coral stone fountain and colourfully uniformed traffic policeman.

'Try Broad Street to start,' he advised, indicating the main avenue running away to the left. 'I'll meet you back here at noon.'

'I'd still prefer it if you gave me some kind of figure to work with,' Erin asserted.

'*I'd* prefer it if you just did as you're told.' Nick glanced at his watch. 'You've got three hours.'

She watched him stride away, wondering who he was going to meet. No teenage infatuant for certain. One was more than enough for any man to deal with.

Samantha tugged at her arm. 'Come on,' she urged. 'We only have three hours!'

Erin stirred herself, adopting a light note. 'I don't imagine you'll be restricted to just this one expedition.'

'I don't intend being restricted to anything,' the younger girl returned airily. 'You heard what Nick said. I'm to have whatever I want.'

Perhaps not in so many words, but that had certainly been the implication, Erin was bound to concede. Who was she to worry about his bank balance, anyway?

Three hours had seemed a reasonable length of time at the outset, but it proved nowhere near long enough for

Samantha to reach saturation point. The presentation of
Nick's card brought them instant attention wherever they
went. Erin did her best to ignore the obvious curiosity when
it became plain that this was strictly a one-sided buying
spree. It was impossible, however, not to feel just a little
covetousness when faced with such a plethora of choice.

One particular dress, with narrow shoulder straps and
softly draped skirt in her favourite blue, really took her
fancy. Samantha urged her to at least try it on, but she
wouldn't, knowing how much harder it would be to say no
once she saw herself in it. Fine feathers, she reminded herself, did not make fine birds. What she had already would
suffice until such time when she could come shopping with
her own money—far in the future though that might be.

By eleven-thirty she could take no more. Samantha had
flatly refused any offers to deliver the goods, leaving the
two of them so loaded with bags they could barely hold
them together.

'We've just time for a drink before we go to meet Nick,'
she said, pausing outside a café. 'I'm so dry, it's either this
or the fountain! Anyway, we can't possibly carry any
more.'

'I suppose not,' agreed Samantha with some reluctance.
'Although there are one or two places we didn't get to look
at yet. Still,' she added on a cheerier note, 'there's always
another day!'

Erin made no comment. She had long since given up
even attempting to keep a tally on what they'd spent this
morning, although it had to be astronomical by any standards. Nick's own fault for failing to lay down a limit, she
told herself, but still felt accountable.

The café was crowded. Looking around for somewhere
to sit, Erin saw one of the two youths seated at a table for
four by the window wave a hand in invitation, and looked
hastily away again. Samantha knew no such hesitation,

ploughing her way between the intervening chairs with scant regard for the people occupying them. Erin followed behind, murmuring apologies which were for the most part accepted with smiles. One of these days, she thought wrathfully, she was going to really blow up!

The lemon trouser suit Samantha had insisted on wearing from the shop added at least a couple of years to her age. Both youths looked her over appreciatively as she dumped all her bags down by the side of one of the spare chairs and collapsed into it with a gamine grin.

'Thanks for the invite. We're just about ready to die of thirst!'

'Hopeless waiting for service,' said the blond-haired young man who had issued the invitation. 'I'll go and fetch some drinks. What do you fancy?'

Not yet seated, Erin put up a staying hand as he started to rise. 'It's all right, thanks. I can go myself.'

'Quicker for me to do it,' he returned easily. 'Tourists tend to get pushed aside.'

'We're not tourists,' said Samantha. 'We live here.'

The interest increased. 'Yeah? How come we never saw you around before?'

'We only got here yesterday,' Erin supplied, reluctantly accepting the offer to buy drinks on the sudden realisation that she didn't have any Bajun currency anyway. 'It's very nice of you,' she added lamely.

'Call it an aloha,' he grinned.

'Wrong island, dummy!' scoffed his companion. 'Wrong ocean, in fact.'

'At the risk of sounding pedantic, the Caribbean's actually a sea not an ocean,' said Erin, dropping her own load of bags and taking a seat. 'Just so we know where we are.'

'Got ya!' chortled the one on his feet. 'I'll be back!'

'I'm Reece Brady,' proffered the other. 'He's Tim Wyman. We live here too.'

'Born and bred?' asked Samantha.

'Tim is. My folks moved here from Michigan when I was a kid.'

He was probably no more than seventeen now, Erin judged. A very good-looking seventeen, she had to admit, with his thick thatch of reddish brown hair and laughing green eyes.

Samantha performed introductions from their own side, drawing a sudden enlightenment when she mentioned Nick's name.

'So you're the ones everybody's talking about!' Reece exclaimed. 'Is he really your uncle?'

'He's my father's younger brother,' said Samantha before Erin could speak. 'Dad didn't leave any money when he died, so we've come to live with Uncle Nick.'

'And relieve him of some of his?' With a meaningful look at the bags strewn about their feet. 'Guess he can afford it. He's loaded!'

'How would *you* know?' demanded Erin brusquely, and received a derisive glance.

'Everybody knows!'

'Knows about what?' asked Tim, returning with a precariously balanced tray.

Reece filled him in on the detail as he set out the glasses, eliciting a gleeful chuckle.

'Dione's going to get a real shock when she gets back!' he exclaimed.

'Who's Dione?' queried Samantha.

'My sister. She helps run the family store—leastways, she does when she's here. She's in New York right now.'

Wyman. Up until now Erin hadn't connected the name with that of one of the stores they had visited this morning. A very up-market store, she recalled.

'What does she have to do with Nick?' she asked on

what she hoped was a casual note, already pretty sure of the answer.

Her use of his name minus the prefix brought a certain speculation to both pairs of eyes, though no comment was made.

'Not quite as much as she'd like,' said Tim. 'Having two gorgeous blondes *in situ* is really going to cramp her style!'

Samantha giggled. 'You don't sound very brotherly.'

'She's not very sisterly. Twenty-six, and full of it! Can't imagine what Nick sees in her.'

'Yes, you can,' Reece grinned. 'The same thing all the guys see in her. A couple of nieces aren't going to make any difference. What Dione wants she goes after, regardless!'

From what had just been said, it was likely that this Dione was the 'certain quarters' Miles Penhalligen had been referring to, thought Erin. If the woman was involved with Nick, she could well imagine her reaction on returning from New York to find this new situation.

His own fault, she told herself defensively. *All* his fault, in fact. If he'd done as she suggested in the first place he wouldn't be faced with any problem at all.

Reaching for the glass of orange juice she had requested, she caught sight of the clock on the far wall and let out a dismayed exclamation.

'We have to go. It's almost twelve!'

'You sound like that fairy-tale character,' scoffed Reece as she began hurriedly to gather the bags together. 'Going to leave us a glass slipper?'

'It surely doesn't matter if we're a bit late,' Samantha protested, making no secret of the fact that she for one was reluctant to abandon their new friends. 'He'll wait.'

'It's been nice talking with you,' Erin told the two boys, ignoring the objection. 'And thanks for the drinks.'

'You've hardly touched them,' Tim pointed out on a disgruntled note.

'I know. I'm sorry.' Unable to offer to pay for them, it was the only thing she could say. 'Come on, Sam.'

She was outside and heading in the direction of the square before the younger girl caught up with her.

'That was real bad manners!' she accused. 'You could at least have let me finish *my* drink, even if you didn't want yours!'

'Nick said he'd see us at noon,' Erin reminded her. 'It would be even more bad-mannered to deliberately keep him waiting. We owe him a lot. More even than we realised.'

Samantha slanted a glance. 'You mean because of what they said back there about Tim's sister? So what? She's only his girlfriend, not his wife. Too bad if she doesn't like us being here.'

Erin had gathered the impression that 'girlfriend' was rather underplaying the relationship. If not Nick's wife—as yet—this Dione was almost certainly his lover. She hated her already.

'It's about time you started showing a little more appreciation,' she said tautly. 'Nick's turned his whole life upside down for our sakes. Not many men in his position would do the same.'

'Most men would think themselves lucky to have two *gorgeous* blondes sharing their home,' came the tongue-in-cheek response.

Erin was unable to stop her lips from curving into a smile, unwilling though she was to give way to it. She only wished she really *was* a gorgeous blonde—preferably one around twenty-six!

It was coming up to a quarter past the hour when they finally reached the square. Nick was waiting by the fountain.

'Sorry we're late,' proffered Erin, surprised by the easy shrug.

'I've known worse time-keeping. Did you get everything you wanted?'

There was no hint of sarcasm in his tone; not that Samantha would have taken any note if there had been, Erin suspected.

'Not *everything*,' she said airily. 'But enough to be going on with.'

'Good.' This time there was a definite dryness. 'No problems?'

'None at all,' Erin confirmed. 'Your name was recognised everywhere.'

He made no comment to that. The surprise would have been, she reflected, if someone had failed to recognise the name.

It was a relief to dump the bags in the car boot—an even greater one to get out of the midday heat. Samantha opted to sit in the back this time, leaving Erin with no choice but to take the front passenger seat. She steeled herself not to draw away when Nick slid in beside her, although his shoulders seemed almost to be brushing hers. The lesser-sized cars might be more sensible for use on the narrow inland roads, but they were too closely confining for comfort.

'We met a Tim Wyman in town,' Samantha imparted when they were on their way. 'Him and his friend, Reece. They bought drinks for us.'

'Non-alcoholic in your case, I hope,' Nick returned. 'They should have been in college, the pair of them.'

'How old are they, then?' she asked.

'Seventeen. They both attend Peterson—the same one you'll be going to come Monday.'

'That soon?' On a disgruntled note.

'The earliest I could arrange. Gives you five full days of freedom.'

Five full weeks wouldn't be enough, Erin could have told him. She waited for Dione's name to come up, but Samantha had other matters on her mind. Erin could almost hear her thinking that if Tim and Reece could get away with playing truant, there was no reason why she shouldn't do the same on occasion. She'd done it often enough back home.

It would be a whole lot better if she were only fourteen herself right now, Erin thought disconsolately. She certainly wouldn't be thinking the way she was about this man at her side. On the other hand, he might see her in a different light if she were older. Nineteen was so betwixt and between. Maybe in October...

She felt a tremor go right through her as her mind leapt ahead to visualise the two of them together, those long, clever fingers exploring every inch of her body, the grey eyes devouring her, wanting her, his shoulders so wide, his body so hard, her arms sliding up about his neck as he...

She put out the tip of her tongue to dampen lips gone suddenly dry, desisting abruptly when Nick glanced her way. This really did have to stop! she thought desperately. The whole thing was getting out of hand.

CHAPTER FIVE

BELLA mellowed a little as the days passed, chiefly due to Erin's efforts to keep both her own and Samantha's room spick and span. As anticipated, the latter's bed-making lasted no longer than the first morning, while the idea of actually tidying up her abandoned clothing never even occurred to her. Erin knew she was as much to blame for the lack of consideration as her sister. It had always been both quicker and easier to do things herself rather than attempt to lay down the law.

Sorting out the build-up of paperwork in the little office at the rear of the studio took no more than a few hours. Inexperienced as she was in business matters, Erin couldn't fail to glean that the sale of art works constituted only a part of Nick's income: he also appeared to have a vast investment portfolio. Not that it made any difference so far as she was concerned. She had known he was wealthy; the degree was of no importance.

His presentation of bank account books and corresponding chequebooks made out in hers and Samantha's names was another matter. The balances added together had to be far in excess of the sum he claimed to have received from the house-clearance firm he had called in that last weekend back home.

Faced with it, he made no attempt to deny it.

'The only way of giving you both a little independence,' he said. 'And no arguments,' he added as she began to form a reply. 'If you don't want to use it, don't, but it's staying right there.'

Erin had collared him in the studio, where he was finishing off the work she had first seen covered on the easel. It was a study of cane cutters at work in the fields, backs bare, muscles gleaming with sweat under the baking sun, the heat almost palpable. Watching the seemingly casual brushstrokes, she envied him his talent. Given all the teaching in the world, she could never have come anywhere close.

'Me aside,' she said, forced to recognise the futility in further protest, 'I don't think it's a very good idea to let Sam loose on this amount of money. She'll probably squander it.'

'On what? More clothes? I'd have thought she had enough to stock a shop already.'

Erin bit her lip. 'I know. I shouldn't have let her spend so much.'

'That wasn't what I meant.' Nick stood back to view the painting, then laid down his brush and palette. 'One of these days,' he continued hardily as he wiped his fingers on a rag, 'you're going to stop reading criticism where there's none intended.'

About to apologise, Erin stopped herself. Right now it would be adding fuel to a fire already smouldering. She half turned to go, pausing as he said her name on a slightly softer note. She could see him in her mind's eye, muscle and sinew contracting, standing there so tall and lean, a comma of dark hair falling across his forehead.

'This is the last of the New York consignment, so we may as well get started on you while you're here,' he said.

'I'm not wearing a nightdress,' she pointed out, and he laughed.

'Preliminary sketches only. I like to do several. Come and sit over here in the light.'

Glad of any legitimate excuse to stay, she did as she was bid, perching on the chair indicated. Nick shifted the easel, setting up another smaller one along with a stool for himself. Erin tried to appear relaxed as he assessed the angles before putting pencil to paper, though it was impossible to feel it under that all-too perceptive gaze.

The paint-spattered T-shirt he was wearing fitted close about the taut swell of his biceps: she could see the movement of muscle beneath the light coating of dark hair on his forearm as he shifted the pencil through both horizontal and vertical axis lines. He was so utterly and devastatingly male: a real man—so different from the boys she had known back home. Not that she'd had much opportunity to meet the opposite sex at all since leaving school.

'Try thinking about something else,' he suggested, obviously aware of her lack of tranquillity. 'Something you'd like to be doing right now.'

There was no trace of irony in his voice. She must stop reading innuendo into every word and gesture, Erin told herself.

All the same, she couldn't stop the images conjured by the words from forming: Nick putting down his pencil and getting to his feet, coming over to lift her bodily from the chair, his face taut with desire, his lips seeking hers. There was a chaise longue over in a corner of the studio. He was carrying her there and laying her down on it, standing back to peel off his shirt and reveal the muscular span of his shoulders and chest, fingers reaching for the buckle of his belt...

She jerked out of it to find the grey eyes viewing her with an expression that brought the hot colour rushing up under her skin. He had a good idea of what had been going through her mind, she realised. It must have been written on her face.

'You've all the time in the world,' he said. 'Don't be in too much of a hurry. And don't bother trying to make out you don't know what I'm talking about either. Just wait for the right man to come along.'

It was too late for denials, Erin conceded in a sudden rush of blood to the head. 'He already did,' she declared. 'I love you, Nick!'

'No, you don't.' His voice had roughened. 'What you're feeling is simple sexual arousal, nothing more. I'm flattered to be the object of it, but that's as far as it goes. Now, be a good girl and forget it.'

'Don't patronise me!' she flashed back. 'I'm not a child. I don't need anyone to tell me what I feel!'

'*I* don't need *this*,' he snapped back. 'Are you going to sit for me, or do we call it a day?'

Trembling with anger and humiliation, her throat too tight for words, Erin got to her feet. Nick made no move to stop her as she headed for the door.

It was several minutes before she could pull herself together sufficiently to take proper stock of what she had said back there, even then unable to believe she could have been so idiotic as to tell a man she had known just one short week that she loved him. What had she expected—reciprocation?

How could she face him again after this? she thought wretchedly. If it were only possible to go home—back where she belonged.

If she used the money in her account, it was possible, she realised. There had to be more than enough for a one-way ticket. She'd be practically destitute when she got there, but anything would be better than staying on here.

And what about Sam? came the reminder. Was she really prepared to turn her back on her sister simply because she'd made a fool of herself? The answer had to be no, of course, leaving her with no alternative but to stick it out the best way she could.

It was gone six when Nick returned to the house. Watching him from her bedroom window as he rounded the pool, Erin wished it were only possible to turn off emotion like turning off a tap. It might not be love, but it was still overwhelming. She had never felt so utterly down-hearted in her life.

Dinner was an ordeal. Having spent the last few days just lazing around the pool, Samantha was becoming bored, and making no effort to conceal it.

'There's not much point in my having all these new things just to wear around here,' she complained. 'I didn't even get to see a beach yet!'

'There's no reason why you shouldn't,' Nick responded. 'Try Paradise on the west side,' he added to Erin. 'It's only a mile or so outside Bridgetown. I'll highlight a route avoiding town on the map. It will be good practice for the school run next week.'

Blue eyes held steady by sheer force of will. 'You're going to trust me with the car?'

'Why not? You hold a valid licence.'

At least they still drove on the left, was Erin's first thought—although the roads between here and the main highway were hardly wide enough for sides to have much meaning. She would have to take careful note of the turns: one cane-bordered lane looked much the same as another.

'You're lucky,' Samantha exclaimed morosely. 'I'm going to be stuck in class for two more years while you're out enjoying yourself!'

'Don't count on leaving at sixteen,' said Nick. 'Erin lost out on extended education. You're not going to do the same.'

'You can't *make* me do anything once I'm sixteen,' she retorted smartly.

'Want to bet?'

Over the course of the past few days, Erin had learned to stay out of any battle of wills between uncle and niece. Nick was more than capable of holding his own. He was doing it now, the spark in his eyes quelling any further outspokenness on Samantha's part—for the time being, at any rate. She applied herself to her dessert with a mulish look on her pretty face.

There was no lingering over coffee tonight. Nick left as soon as he'd finished. Erin wasn't surprised to hear a car departing some twenty minutes later. He had obviously had enough of the pair of them.

It was a long evening, made even longer by Samantha's disgruntlement over Erin's refusal to take the other car and drive down to town.

'I can't see why not,' she said. 'It only takes about twenty minutes.'

'In daylight, and for someone who knows where they're going,' Erin pointed out. 'We'd probably finish up thoroughly lost.'

'Even that would be more exciting than just sitting around out here night after night!' The younger girl shoved herself to her feet. 'I'm going to watch television!'

So far as Erin was concerned, the Caribbean evening was one of the best parts of the day, but she could understand Sam's frustration. Luxury living was no substitute for the action-packed lifestyle she had anticipated.

At least she would have school to occupy her come Monday. What she herself was going to do with her time Lord only knew. Sitting for Nick was definitely out. He'd probably lost interest in painting her anyway.

She felt sorry for him, stuck with a situation no man his age could possibly relish. He had done what he considered the right thing in bringing them to his home, but he had to be regretting it by now.

He still hadn't returned when she turned in at ten. Not that she would have expected it. Samantha was in her room reading a magazine, her mood considerably lighter.

'We'll make our own fun,' she declared when Erin popped her head round the door to say goodnight. 'Starting tomorrow when we go find that beach. It's Sunday. We might even run into Tim and Reece down there.'

'We might at that,' Erin agreed, too relieved to find her sister's flag flying high again to point out the unlikelihood of their choosing the same stretch of sand. 'See you at breakfast.'

Undressed, she found herself too restless for sleep. There were chairs on the balcony. She went out to take one, propping her legs on another to contemplate the moonlit scene below. If this afternoon's episode had achieved nothing else, it had made her grow up at last. From now on she kept her feelings under lock and key.

It was hot tonight, the trade winds no more than a waft of warm air against her cheek. The pool looked so inviting, twinkling out there beneath the stars. On impulse, she got up again and went back indoors to seize her one costume from the shower stall where she had hung it to dry this morning, only now remembering that it had split right along the side seam as she'd taken it off.

One of Samantha's new ones would probably fit her okay, but it went against the grain to go borrowing—especially if she had to wake her up to ask.

So what was wrong with skinny-dipping? she thought recklessly. Bella and Josh were over in their own home, and Nick probably wouldn't be back for ages—if he came back at all. It could even be that Dione had returned to the island, hence his hurry to depart. If the woman had her own place—and it seemed more than likely that she would—then he might well spend the night with her.

Erin shut off that train of thought abruptly. The house was silent as she crept downstairs, her bare feet making no sound on the thick carpeting. It was quickest and easiest to let herself out via the French doors from the living room. Reaching the pool, she dropped the towel she had brought from the bathroom and stripped off her nightdress before she could change her mind, letting herself down into the water instead of diving in, so that she wouldn't cause a splash.

The water felt like silk against her bare skin. She swam slowly round the island, relishing the wonderful sense of freedom in being at one, so to speak, with Nature. A dozen different scents tickled her nostrils, more emotive by night even than by day.

The sky was cloudless, the stars brilliant in their setting of coal-black velvet. Erin floated on her back to gaze at them, mind emptied of everything but the sheer delight in being so totally unrestricted. She could spend eternity like this, supported in the soft caress of the water, her hair spread like a butterfly's wings about her head, her limbs boneless.

A shadow blocked out the moon, resolving itself into a tall dark figure standing on the pool-edge watching her. Erin continued to float there, too far under the spell of the night to recognise reality.

'It's heaven!' she murmured. 'You should try it.'

Face in shadow, Nick made no verbal reply. When he moved it was with almost robotic purpose, unbuttoning his shirt and shrugging it from his shoulders, flicking open his belt to slide the zip and discard his trousers. He was wearing black jockey shorts beneath, but only for a moment. The ripples when he let himself down into the water spread into a widening fan as he forged a passage to her.

It was only when he seized hold of her that Erin knew this was no dream. He felt too devastatingly real to be a figment of imagination. She shut out everything but the messages reaching her through her senses, fingers sliding up over smooth wet muscle to lock behind the dark head as he found her mouth with his in a kiss that rocketed her from girlhood to womanhood once and for all.

The water was shallow enough here for him to stand.

Erin felt the tremoring start deep as he brought the lower half of her body into closer contact with his. He was already fully aroused; instinctively, she opened her legs a little, to fit herself even closer, feeling him slide between her thighs, her insides turning liquid—molten fire reaching down into every extremity.

He hadn't so far said a word; nor did she want him to for fear of breaking the spell. Black as the sky above in this light, his eyes held a glitter to rival the stars. She clung to him as he lifted her legs about his waist, tensing momentarily at the first pressuring touch but too far gone to resist the urge coursing through her.

He claimed her mouth once more, parting her lips with the tip of his tongue to taste the inner sweetness. She gave a muffled gasp as the pressure between her thighs increased to almost unbearable proportions for a fleeting moment, then the pain was gone and they were wholly and wonderfully together, his body possessing her, filling her, beginning to move, his hands cupping her buttocks to move her in tune with him, his lips sealing her involuntary cries—all thought suspended as the world spun crazily about her head...

She awoke to early-morning light, disorientated for a moment until memory came flooding back, bringing with it a sense of fantasy. Had last night really happened?

Erin put out the tip of her tongue to touch her lips, conscious of a pleasurable ache in her lower regions, a tenderness no dream could have produced. It had happened all right. Every last sensational moment! She closed her eyes again, the better to savour the memories: seeing Nick standing there, so lean and powerful in his nudity, feeling the excitement rising in her at the mere thought of all he'd done to her. She wished he was here right now, ready to do it all again. Never in a thousand years could she have enough of him!

The euphoria faded a little as she recalled the change in him when he'd brought her indoors. He'd packed her off to bed with scarcely a word, much less a goodnight kiss. Not that he had anything to regret. If anyone was to blame for what had happened between them it was her, for enticing him. Men were notoriously weak when it came to resisting temptation.

Anyway, *she* had no regrets. Neither would he once he realised she wasn't going to go all clingy on him now. Not that she wouldn't be over the moon if he did come to feel the same way about her that she felt about him, of course. At any rate, there was nothing to stop them from sharing a bed some nights. No one else need know.

It was still very early. She was tempted to slip along to his room right now and waken him with a kiss. She could visualise the way he would look with his hair tousled, his jaw bristly. His chest would be bare; she didn't see him wearing a pyjama jacket. After last night, it hardly mattered if he was wearing nothing at all.

She was out of bed as she thought about it, too stimulated by the prospect of seeing him again to lend an ear to any cautionary voice. Bella wouldn't be over for at least another hour. All the time in the world for whatever might happen.

Nick's bedroom lay at the far end of the landing. It was most unlikely that Samantha would be awake at this hour, or that she would hear footsteps on the thick carpeting if she was, but Erin found herself tiptoeing past just in case. Nick's door wasn't locked. Gingerly depressing the handle, she eased it open, peeping round it to see a king-sized bed across a wide expanse of dark green carpet.

He lay on his stomach, face turned away from her towards the window, arms curved around the pillow. The single sheet was pushed down below his waistline, confirm-

ing her guess that pyjamas were not his style. A shaft of
sunlight outlined the powerful shoulders.

Erin damped down the excitement swelling inside her
and ventured further into the room, closing the door softly
behind her. It seemed to take an age to cross the yards of
carpet; any moment she expected him to waken up and roll
over. Reaching the bed at last, she allowed herself a moment of delicious contemplation, running a slow gaze from
the dark head down the line of his back to the firm swell
of his behind. There was no surplus flesh anywhere, just
hard muscle. But she already knew that, of course.

As usual, she hadn't bothered to put anything on her feet.
Without pausing to consider, she slipped off her nightdress
and lifted the sheet to slide very gently into the bed beside
him. He stirred, and murmured something, then settled
again. Erin put her face closer, to inhale the emotive masculine scent of his skin, unable to stop herself from pressing
a feather-light kiss to his nape.

She froze for a moment when he rolled over to face her,
relaxing when his eyes remained closed, his breathing reg-
ulated. It was too late to start changing her mind now anyway, she told herself. She was bound to waken him getting
out of the bed again.

His face in close-up was just as she had imagined it,
tanned skin smooth over brow and cheekbone, jawline dark
with morning stubble. Never having had the luxury of
studying him in such detail before, she hadn't fully realised
how long his eyelashes were, or just how well shaped his
mouth.

The sheet had slid even lower when he turned. She
dropped her gaze down the strong column of his throat to
a chest lightly coated in dark hair that tapered away to
merge with ridged stomach muscle. Dormant, he was still
impressive. Pulses racing, insides on fire, Erin reached

down a hand to gently enclose him, thrilled to feel an immediate pulsing response.

Nick drew in a long, slow breath, mouth curving. 'Good morning to you too,' he said softly.

Erin formed a smile of her own as the grey eyes opened. 'Hi!' she said.

For a brief moment there was no reaction, then he thrust himself upright, face darkened, eyes blazing. 'What the hell do you think you're doing?' he demanded.

Shaken to the core by the force of his anger, Erin sought refuge in sarcasm. 'You didn't say that last night!'

The anger died, the expression that replaced it no more encouraging. 'It shouldn't have happened,' he admitted wryly. 'I thought I could handle it.'

'Handle what?' she asked.

'Wanting you.' His voice was suddenly savage again. 'Wanting a nineteen-year-old kid!'

'I'm not a kid,' she protested. 'I wanted you too. You know I did.'

'You didn't even know *what* you wanted.'

'Yes, I did. I've known the facts of life since I was about ten.'

Nick said something short and sharp under his breath. 'I'm not talking about basic biology!'

'Neither am I.' The words formed themselves. 'I was telling you the truth yesterday, Nick. I love you. Wanting is a part of loving, isn't it?'

His lips curved in a mirthless smile. 'Not always.'

'If you're saying you don't love me, I already know, and it doesn't matter.' That was a downright lie, but she wasn't about to admit it. 'I'm happy just being with you.'

'It *isn't* going to happen again,' he declared. 'Once might still be one time too many.'

'If you're worried I might get pregnant, you needn't,' she said. 'I've been on the Pill for the last three months.'

His brows drew together. 'Why?'

'Women's problems.'

The scowl deepened. 'Don't get clever with me!'

'I'm not trying to be clever,' she denied. 'The doctor put me on it for "regulatory purposes"—to use his own words. You're the only one I've ever made love with.'

'I already gathered that.'

'Then you'll know how special you are to me. I really do—'

'Don't start trying to tell me you love me again,' he cut in roughly before she could voice the words. 'You've no idea what love is.'

Blue eyes flared. 'Will *you* stop telling *me* what I do or don't feel! What are you afraid of—that I'll expect you to marry me? Well, you needn't be! I'm no more interested in marriage than you are!'

'So exactly how *do* you see yourself?' he asked with obvious scepticism. 'As my live-in lover?'

'If you want me to be.' Erin softened both expression and voice. '*Do* you want me, Nick?'

The tell-tale muscle jerked in his jawline as he surveyed her slender curves. 'Get out of here,' he said thickly. 'Now!'

Her smile was slow, her confidence fully restored by what was happening to him regardless. 'You don't mean that.' She raised her arms to slide both hands behind her head beneath the spread of sun-kissed fair hair, seeing the effect on him as her breasts lifted into pert prominence and aware of a wholly new sense of power. 'Do you?' she whispered.

His teeth came together with an audible snap. When he moved it was with controlled violence, rolling to the far edge of the bed to sit up with his back to her.

'You've got ten seconds,' he said grimly. 'I'm serious, Erin. I want you out!'

She came to a sitting position herself, eyeing the tapering back irresolutely. She could take the coward's way out and obey him, or defy him and accept the consequences—whatever they might be.

He stiffened when she slid a fingertip down the ridge of his spine. 'It already happened,' she murmured. 'What difference is it going to make if it happens again? I told you there's no danger of my getting pregnant.'

'There's no such thing as a hundred per cent guarantee, you little fool,' he gritted.

'There was no guarantee at all so far as you knew beforehand,' Erin felt moved to point out. 'It didn't stop you then.'

He gave a short, hard laugh. 'The way you looked floating in that damned pool, wild horses couldn't have stopped me! That's something I have to live with.'

'If you used something yourself this time, there wouldn't be any risk at all,' she said, trying to sound practical about it. She bent to put her lips where her finger had been, extending the tip of her tongue to taste the faint saltiness of his skin, the clamour mounting by the second inside her. 'I'm not leaving,' she stated recklessly, 'so you'd better reconcile yourself. I *want* you, Nick! Now! This minute!'

For a moment or two, when he made no attempt to remove the hands she slid over his shoulders, she really thought she'd won through. The sudden jerk as he stood up tore her hands from him and left her kneeling there numbly watching as he moved with purpose over to the nearby chair to take up a silk robe and slide into it.

When he turned, he was in control, face taut. 'It isn't me you want,' he said. 'It's just sex. My fault, I admit, for giving you the taste, but this is as far as it goes. Now, are you going to go, or do I have to put you out?'

It was on the tip of Erin's tongue to issue a challenge,

but she held it back. He still wanted her, and they both knew it, but there was no doubting his adamancy.

Unselfconscious in her nudity until this moment, she felt herself flushing beneath the hardened gaze as she slid back across the bed to find the nightdress she had discarded. She was glad of the curtain of hair falling forward about her face as she pulled it on. The boldness had flown; all she felt now was rejected.

'Are you going to send me back home?' she asked in muffled tones.

'It would be the sensible thing to do,' he said. 'Better from both points of view.' He added tersely, 'Though not until I can be sure there are no repercussions.'

Erin forced herself to say it. 'And if there did turn out to be?'

The pause seemed to stretch for ever. 'Something we'd have to deal with,' he said at length. 'Don't you have any slippers?'

She shook her head, avoiding any direct contact with the grey eyes for fear of losing what little self-respect she still had and begging him not to send her back. 'I'll try and stay out of your way,' she declared stiffly. 'Sorry to have been such a nuisance.'

She made her escape before he could respond—if he'd intended responding at all—closing the door on him in a welter of self-disparagement. If she hadn't made a fool of herself before, she'd certainly done the trick this morning.

Nick was wrong about one thing, though; it was more than just sex. The thought of never seeing him again if he really did make her leave Barbados was unbearable.

CHAPTER SIX

THE school run down to St Thomas proved no great problem. By the end of that first week Erin felt she could almost have done it blindfold.

Samantha settled down surprisingly quickly once over the initial strangeness. As schools went, it wasn't bad, she admitted. Everyone was being really friendly. Three years above her, Tim Wyman had taken it upon himself to introduce her around the very first day, which had certainly helped.

Life would be a whole lot simpler if she was in the same age group, thought Erin with some envy, listening to her sister relate the week's happenings over breakfast on the Saturday morning. It was probably true that schooldays were the happiest days of one's life, even if it didn't always appear so at the time.

She stole a glance at Nick, seated opposite, wondering what was really going on inside the dark head as he gazed out past her at the sun-bathed landscape. He'd taken care to keep contact between them to a minimum this past week, which might have been best from his point of view but had simply served to increase her hunger.

The nights were the worst time: she would lie there for ages, unable to sleep, her whole body aching for the touch of those supple, sensitive hands, her mouth yearning for his kisses. If only he would forget the circumstances and just let things happen the way they were obviously meant to happen!

He switched his gaze suddenly, meeting her eyes with

inscrutable expression. Heart jerking, Erin said the first thing that came into her head.

'I was thinking of driving down to town. One or two things I need to get.'

'You don't need to explain,' he returned. 'The car's there whenever you need it.' He paused. 'You might consider getting yourself at least one new outfit while you're down there. We'll be going out tonight.'

Samantha's interest perked up. '*All* of us?'

'All of us,' he confirmed.

'To where?' asked Erin, quelling the urge to say she wasn't going anywhere with him while he kept up this pretence that nothing had happened between them.

'The Wymans' place down on the coast. Yes, that Wyman,' he added before Samantha could frame the obvious question. 'I know Tim's father.'

'He must be a piece older than you are to have a daughter of twenty-six,' observed Erin with deliberation, and saw the grey eyes sharpen.

'How do you know about the daughter?'

'Tim told us about her when we met in town that first day,' Samantha chimed in, looking at her most innocent. 'You know her quite well too, don't you?'

Nick gave no sign of having registered the nuances. 'Val's in his early fifties, if it matters. There's another son in between Dione and Tim. Harley's twenty-three.'

Samantha giggled. 'They must have run out of ideas when it came to naming Tim!'

'Why would the two of us be invited?' asked Erin bluntly.

'They want to meet you.'

'Why?'

Nick drew an impatient breath. 'Are you trying to rile me?'

Blue eyes widened in bland imitation of younger ones. 'Why would I do that?'

'If I hear that word once more—' He broke off, shaking his head as if in repudiation of what he had been about to say. 'You're invited, that's it. We'll be leaving here around eight.' Abruptly pushing back his chair, he got to his feet. 'I'll be in the studio.'

The crates had arrived yesterday. She could have been over there helping him pack them if she hadn't chosen to go skinny-dipping that night, thought Erin. Not that she would be without the memory; it was all she had to sustain her.

'What's with you and Nick?' asked Samantha curiously. 'I thought he was going to let go with something really nasty just then!'

Erin forced a smile, a light shrug. 'Just a difference of opinion. Are you coming into town with me?'

'You bet!' Successfully sidetracked, the younger girl pushed back her own chair. 'I'll go and change. You never know who we might meet!'

Erin watched her go, too lacking in enthusiasm to make any immediate move herself. Nick's suggestion that she buy a new outfit had been more in the nature of an order. While what she wore round here was of no importance to him, he obviously didn't want her looking like the poor relation in front of his friends.

It would be discourteous to refuse the invitation, so a new outfit it had to be. If the dress she had seen before was still available, and it fitted okay, she would settle for that. Probably not a patch on what others would be wearing, but who was going to notice?

The dress was not only still available, it fitted as if it was made for her. Samantha clapped her hands when she saw it on.

'You look absolutely super!' she exclaimed generously.

'Don't ever try to tell me that nice clothes don't make a difference! It's added at least three years for a start!'

Whatever hesitation Erin had still entertained, that latter statement clinched the decision for her. And the wisp of a high-heeled sandal Samantha urged her to try on with the dress gave her a poise she had never possessed before. Viewing herself in the long dressing mirror, she felt a stirring of excitement at the thought of Nick seeing her like this. She even had cleavage!

'You'll wow them all tonight,' Sam declared with confidence when they emerged onto the street again. 'I wonder what this Harley's like?'

Erin didn't care. The only person she was interested in wowing was Nick. If she failed to make him want her again, it wasn't going to be for lack of trying, she vowed.

He didn't put in an appearance for lunch. He'd left soon after they had themselves this morning, Bella advised. No, she didn't know where he'd gone. She didn't go asking the master his business.

'You really think of him as "the master"?' asked Samantha, tongue tucked well into cheek.

'It a courtesy title,' replied the Bajan woman severely. 'It be good for you to show some respec' too.'

'He'd think I was being the dead opposite if *I* started calling him that!' Sam laughed. 'Lighten up, Bell! It's the twentieth century now!'

Muttering, Bella swept off along the veranda. Erin gave her sister a reproving frown.

'You shouldn't tease her like that.'

Samantha pulled a face back. 'Don't be such a grump! You're getting more like Bella every day!' She gave another laugh. 'I wonder what "maulsprigging" means.'

Erin had a very good notion. There were times when she too thought her sister might benefit from a well-placed smack.

They spent the afternoon around the pool. At the last moment Erin had added a yellow bikini to her purchases. Wearing it now, she felt slightly conspicuous, aware of the faint demarcation lines about her midriff and hoping they would soon fill in. At least with Sam there were no detrimental comparisons in other departments; her sister's breasts were still in the earlier stages of development.

Not that the smallness of her own had appeared in any way off-putting to a certain party, she conceded, thoughts harking back as always to that tumultuous occasion. Her nipples started tingling at the very memory of how it had felt to be enclosed within those firm lips, his tongue a flickering flame against her skin. Making love was the most wonderful sensation in the world! She wanted, needed, *yearned* for it to happen again. Only not just with anyone, of course. If she couldn't have Nick, she would stay celibate for the rest of her life!

Opening her eyes to see him poised on the pool-edge in the act of diving in, it was almost as if she had conjured him up by the very power of her longing. She watched avidly as he cleaved the water with scarcely a splash, the strong, clean lines of his body imprinted on her retinae. The black trunks he was wearing were brief enough, but she had seen him minus even those. Her inner thigh muscles went into involuntary spasm just thinking about the way he had looked then.

'Show-off!' said Samantha, watching him too as he executed a fast crawl down the length of the pool and around the little island. 'Not that he hasn't got a lot to show off,' she allowed. 'Dad never had muscles like that for sure!'

'Your father didn't have the time to exercise,' Erin felt bound to defend.

'You mean he didn't have the inclination,' came the unimpressed return. 'He might have lived a lot longer if he'd kept himself fit.'

Erin couldn't argue with that. In the years after her mother's death, her stepfather must have put on at least twenty pounds. If genes had any bearing at all, Nick might be expected to have a battle with weight gain himself as he got older, but she doubted if he would ever allow it to get out of hand.

She could imagine him at fifty, hair silver grey at the temples, perhaps a few lines radiating out from the corners of his eyes. When he was fifty, she would be thirty-five— a mature woman—maybe even a mother. Two children, she thought dreamily: a boy and a girl, in that order. The boy would look just like his father; the girl would take after her.

Nick hauled himself out of the pool, snapping her back to reality. There was about as much chance of that particular daydream coming to fruition as the world coming to an end next Tuesday, she reflected wistfully.

'Terrific style!' applauded Samantha as he ran both hands through his hair to squeeze out excess moisture. 'Not a bad bod either, for an old man.'

'All reassurances gratefully received,' he grinned. 'I hope you're wearing plenty of sun lotion.'

'We both are,' she confirmed, not in the least fazed by the oblique reference to the brevity of her bikini. 'I finally got Erin into one.'

'So I see.' The smile was still there as the grey eyes shifted to the other reclining figure, though altered a little in character. 'Very fetching too.'

'You wait till you see her tonight!' Sam enthused, still in a generous mood. 'You'll have to fight all the guys off!'

'I'll do my best,' he said, registering Erin's discomfiture. 'Either of you fancy a drink? Non-alcoholic,' he added as Samantha started to reply.

'As if I'd ask for anything but,' she retorted in wide-eyed indignation. 'Iced pineapple juice for me, please.'

'I'll have the same, thanks,' said Erin, having difficulty in thinking straight about anything at the moment.

Nick moved off towards the house, the moisture drying on him as he went. Erin tore her eyes from the departing back to find Samantha looking at her with a sly smile on her face.

'You like him, don't you?' she said. 'I mean *really* like!'

Erin kept her voice level with an effort. 'Of course I like him. He's been very good to us both.'

'That's not what I mean, and you know it! You've got the hots for him.'

'Where did you pick *that* little gem up?' Erin demanded, using disgust as a shield.

Sam grinned again. 'Don't come over all high and mighty. It only means—'

'I know what it means. I just don't like hearing you say it.'

'All right, then, I'll put it another way. You'd like to go to bed with him, wouldn't you?'

Erin could do nothing to stop the tell-tale colour from flooding her cheeks. Her, 'Don't be ridiculous!' sounded weak even to her own ears.

'It's nothing to get in a strop about,' her sister returned imperturbably. 'I might even fancy him a bit myself if I were your age.'

Erin sat up abruptly. 'You shouldn't be thinking about fancying anybody at your age!'

'Oh, come on! I'm fourteen, not nine! I fancy Tim like mad.'

'You watch far too much television.' It was all Erin could come up with on the spur of the moment. Sam had always been a bit precocious, but this was reaching new levels! She added hesitantly, 'You wouldn't do anything...foolish?'

'I'm not stupid either.' The tone was derisive. 'I'm not going to finish up like Maureen Bailey back home!'

There was a chance yet that *she* might, thought Erin, recalling what Nick had said about the lack of fail-safe. A very small chance, she assured herself, aware of a part of her that actually wished it would happen.

She made no further comment, too afraid of what she might inadvertently give away. Nick returned bearing three tall frosted glasses on a tray, setting it down on the low round table between the two girls. There was a spare lounger laid out on Erin's far side. Taking up his own glass, he moved round to seat himself on it.

Sam took a single long swallow from her glass, then put it down and got to her feet.

'I'm going in again,' she announced. 'I want to wash my hair before we go out.'

'Me too,' Erin agreed, seizing on the excuse. 'I suppose I'd better get started, in fact. It takes ages to dry!'

'In a minute.' Nick spoke quietly but with purpose. 'We have to talk.'

Erin subsided with mixed emotions, waiting until her sister was in the water before saying tonelessly, 'We've had all week to talk.'

'Don't make this any harder than it has to be,' he admonished. 'I'm not here to make excuses for what I did the other night. It was totally—'

'Wonderful!' she interjected, throwing caution to the winds along with any last remnants of pride. 'You don't need to make excuses. You didn't take advantage of me. I knew what I was doing. *And* I'd do it again,' she added boldly.

His lips twitched at the corners. 'You just don't know how to take no for an answer, do you?'

'I would if I knew it was really meant,' she said, emboldened still further by the flash of humour in the grey eyes. 'You might regret it happening, but it doesn't stop you wanting me. That's why you've steered clear all week, isn't it? You're afraid you might let yourself be tempted again.'

Humour gave way to a swift-growing intolerance. 'You've no idea what you're talking about,' he said grimly. 'You're—'

'Only a kid?' she cut in again, determined not to give way. 'If I was, I stopped being one a week ago, so please stop treating me as one! It's too late to go back.'

'Do you think I don't realise it?' he growled. 'I started something there's no going back on!'

Erin shook her head emphatically. 'You didn't start it, it was already there—just waiting for the right person to come along at the right time and let it out.'

Nick didn't answer immediately, regard narrowed to her face, framed within the fall of bright hair. When he did speak it was with deliberation. 'Except that it was the wrong person and the wrong time.'

'Why?' Erin demanded.

'I'm too old for you, for one thing.'

'No, you're not!' she denied fiercely. 'Lots of men have relationships with younger women.'

The dark brows lifted sardonically. 'You've seen it happen so often, of course.'

He was laughing at her now, she sensed, and not in any kind way. 'I don't need to see it to know it happens,' she said with what dignity she could marshal. 'I'm going to wash my hair.'

This time he made no attempt to stop her as she got up from the lounger, nor did he say anything more, laying himself down with an air of resignation. So much for talking, Erin reflected wryly.

She spent a long time over her hair. It was coming up

to seven-thirty before it was fully dried. Falling loose about her shoulders, it made her look depressingly young.

Rooting through her things, she came up with a packet of hairpins she had acquired some time ago and never yet used, and managed to secure a thick coil on top of her head. Neck and shoulders bared, the slightly dipped front of the blue dress revealing a glimpse of lightly tanned curves, she looked very different from the girl who had arrived here almost two weeks ago. An improvement for certain.

If she'd had any doubts at all left on that score, they were banished by the look in Nick's eyes as she descended the stairs to where he waited in the hall.

'Sam wasn't exaggerating,' was all he said, but it was enough.

He looked devastating himself, in a pale cream tuxedo that made his shoulders appear even broader. It took every ounce of control Erin possessed to keep her emotions from visibly surfacing.

'You didn't say it was a formal affair,' she managed with creditable lightness.

'It isn't,' he said. 'Not the way you mean, at least. Val and his wife believe in making the most of any occasion, and like their guests to follow the same code. I didn't want you to feel uncomfortable.'

Which she would have done, Erin was bound to admit, in any of her other garments. She'd been acting like an idiot in refusing to replenish her wardrobe. Nick had every reason to consider her an ungrateful wretch. First thing Monday she would go down into town again and settle that situation at least. As to the rest...

Sam's arrival broke off the thought before it crystallised. Wearing a short, off-white tunic that exposed rather too much leg, her eyes and lips emphasised with make-up, she looked not only older than her years but a bit tarty to boot, in Erin's estimation. She expected Nick to order an immediate removal of the eyeliner, if nothing else, but he made no comment, leaving her with the impression that such matters were her province if anyone's.

'Shall we go?' he said while she was still trying to come up with some unhurtful way of putting it across. 'It's gone eight already.'

Built in Spanish style, with arched entrances and fretted iron window grilles, the Wyman villa lay in a private cove near Holetown on the west coast. The huge lounge occupying the greater part of one jutting wing already held a regular throng of people, most of them older than Nick, all of them well dressed.

The dark-haired woman who came to greet them was in her late forties, at a guess, her smile purely social as she welcomed the two girls. Erin had the distinct impression that *her* appearance had come as something of a surprise.

'You'll find Tim out on the patio,' she said to Samantha. 'He'll look after you.' Her expression warmed as she turned her attention back to Nick. 'I imagine you already knew Dione was planning on cutting her New York visit short?'

'As a matter of fact, no,' he returned. 'When did she get in?'

'Just an hour ago. She's still in the process of deciding what to wear. You know how long that can take!'

Nick laughed and shrugged. 'I'll expect her when I see her. Are your in-laws here tonight?'

'They are,' she confirmed. 'I don't think you've met Shirley's daughter and her husband. I organised this affair to welcome them back as full-time residents at last. They own Bay Marris.'

Nick looked interested. 'Lovely place!'

'Isn't it, though! It's been run as a country club for years, of course, but they're turning it back into a private residence now—although they'll still allow the golf course to be used. Bryn's a top-flight construction consultant—or he

was. Tessa's spent most of her married life chasing all over
the world after him, poor dear!'

'I suppose she felt it worth it just to be with him,' said
Erin, knowing she certainly would if she were ever in that
position.

Pamela Wyman gave her a condescending glance. 'The
same romantic notion Tessa had. She was about the same
age as you when she married Bryn. They never found time
to have children.' The last in the complacent manner of one
who had found time to produce three. 'Shirley will introduce you. They're all of them outside at the moment. Val
too, I think.'

She turned on the smile again to greet the couple just
entering the room. 'Paul—Melissa! How lovely to see you!'

Nick put a light hand beneath Erin's elbow and steered
her clear of the welcome pad. 'Let's find the younger element for you.'

'I'd like to meet these other people,' she said, with no
intention of being ditched. 'They must have led a fascinat-
ing life!'

'A pretty hard one at times, I'd imagine.' He sounded
tolerant. 'Come on, then.'

A loggia laced through with bougainvillaea gave onto a
broad patio with an oval swimming pool at its centre.
Beyond that, through a curtain of palm trees, lay the beach
itself, both sand and sea shimmering in the moonlight. The
cicadas were loud and fluid, rising even above the combined chatter and laughter issuing from the various small
groups of people scattered about.

Still holding her elbow in that same light grasp, Nick led
Erin to one of the nearer groups seated about a slatted
wooden table, bending to kiss the cheek of a silver-haired
woman whose looks belied the age she had to be if she
was the mother of the younger version seated next to her.

'Good to see you, Shirley,' he said. 'You too, Roland,

Val.' He looked across at two men with roughly the same age difference between them. 'I'd like you to meet my niece—or one of them, at any rate. This is Erin. Samantha is over there with Tim.'

Shirley Wyman's smile put her daughter-in-law's in the shade. 'How do you like Barbados, Erin?'

'I love it!' she said, smiling back. 'Both Samantha and I are *so* grateful to Uncle Nick for letting us come to live with him!'

The other, younger woman bit her lip as if to control a laugh, her eyes dancing. 'You must be,' she said. 'I'm Tessa Marshall. This is my husband, Bryn.' She indicated the man who had risen from his seat on the arm of her chair to stretch out a hand in greeting to the pair of them. 'It's so unusual to find a man your age willing to take on such a responsibility,' she added to Nick.

'It poses no problem,' he returned easily. 'Erin takes care of her sister, the way she's always done.' The hand still under her elbow had tightened its grasp, as if in warning against any further facetiousness. 'She's eager to hear all about your travels.'

Tessa laughed. 'It'll have to be the potted version. Life isn't long enough for all the detail.' She patted the empty chair at her side. 'Come and sit by me.'

'You don't know what you're letting yourself in for,' warned her husband on a humorous note as Erin obeyed. 'She'll have *your* life story out of you before you know it.' He turned his attention to Nick. 'I'm a great admirer of your work. Do you take on commissions?'

'He's going to ask if he'll do a portrait of me to hang at Bay Marris now we're home for good,' said Tessa wryly. 'I hope Nick won't mind being collared so soon. Bryn doesn't believe in hanging back.'

'I'm sure Nick would be only too pleased to paint you,'

Erin assured her. 'You're a very beautiful woman. So is your mother.'

'Yes, you'd never believe she's in her seventies, would you?' Tessa sounded gratified. 'You remind me very much of myself when I was your age, Erin. I had long blonde hair and a slinky figure too back then.'

She had a good figure still, from what she could see, Erin considered, but decided it would sound a mite syco-phantic to say so. 'Mrs Wyman said you were about my age when you married Bryn,' she said instead.

'Sweet nineteen,' the other confirmed. 'Bryn's twelve years older, although you wouldn't guess it now. Men are so fortunate that way. Greying hair just makes them look distinguished. He and Nick share a certain similarity, wouldn't you say? Allowing for the years between, of course. How old is he?'

'Thirty-four.' Erin was watching the two men as they talked, realising that Bryn did indeed quite closely resemble the image she had created in her mind that afternoon. 'Fif-teen years,' she murmured, only becoming aware that she had said it out loud when she looked back to meet a pair of comprehending green eyes.

'Not unsurmountable,' Tessa said softly. 'In fact, the way he was holding onto you just now, I'd say the odds were very much in favour.'

There was no point, Erin decided ruefully, in trying to deny what she had made so patently obvious. 'That was just to stop me calling him Uncle Nick again,' she admitted. 'I'm not really his niece, of course. His brother was my stepfather.'

Tessa smiled. 'I'd gathered it was something like that from the way you reacted. I suppose it's simpler for him to introduce you that way rather than go into explana-tions—although it could make things a little difficult for you both.'

The others were all engrossed in their own conversations—Nick himself too far away now to overhear anything they were saying anyway. Erin lifted her shoulders in a wry little shrug, feeling drawn to this woman who had known what it was like to fall in love with an older man. 'It's hardly likely to matter.'

'That's defeatist talk!' Tessa kept her voice low, but the cogency came through loud and clear. 'Age doesn't have any bearing on how you feel about someone. I fell in love with Bryn when I was fourteen.'

'Did he feel the same way?'

'Yes. He waited five years for me to grow up.' She gave a reminiscent smile. 'Not that it was plain sailing even then, but we've had twenty-seven wonderful years together—and plenty more to come.'

Erin did a quick mental calculation, her eyes widening. 'That makes you forty-six and Bryn fifty-eight! I can hardly believe it!'

'Love keeps the wrinkles at bay.' Tessa was obviously appreciative of the compliment. 'There might be a few men who can look at a young and lovely girl without wanting her, but I doubt if your Nick is one of them.' Catching the fleeting expression in Erin's eyes, she gave a sage nod. 'You're halfway there already.'

Erin bit back the instinctive denial, recognising the unlikelihood of being believed. 'You're not shocked?' she asked.

Tessa smiled again. 'The way you obviously feel about him, there's nothing to be shocked about. I once pushed Bryn fully clothed into a swimming pool in the hope that he'd lose the control he was exercising at the time and do what I wanted him to do.'

'And...did he?'

'No, much to my disappointment. A bit *too* strong on will-power at times, my husband.'

Glancing his way in quick appraisal, Erin could imagine. Nick was strong-willed too, but she had managed to undermine him in little more than a week, which surely had to mean something.

Tessa was right, she decided in sudden surging determination: she *was* halfway there. Whatever it took to go the rest of the way, she was up to it!

A cheer went up from the group gathered nearest the house, followed by laughter and greetings as some newcomer emerged from within to join the party. Erin saw Nick look across, his expression altering.

Turning her head to follow his gaze, she felt her heart drop like a stone as she viewed the woman making her way towards him. If this was Dione, the battle was over before it had begun!

CHAPTER SEVEN

JET-BLACK hair drawn back from a smooth oval of a face, voluptuously curved body poured into a classic black tube of a dress, the new arrival had just about every male eye in the vicinity riveted to her, but her smile was directed only at one.

'Surprise!' she said.

'Not any longer,' Nick returned equably. 'Why the change of plan?'

'I just couldn't stay away any longer darling!' She kissed him lightly on the lips. 'Missed me?'

'Some,' he allowed, eliciting a provocative pout.

'I'll be looking for a little more enthusiasm later.'

'In vain, if he's any sense,' said Tessa *sotto voce*. She returned her husband's meaningful glance blandly.

If Nick had heard the comment, he gave no sign, and Dione had already moved on to greet some other people. Erin felt as flat as a burst balloon. Why would Nick want her any more when he had all that for the taking? Dione obviously didn't mind who knew what their relationship was.

'I have to find the bathroom,' she murmured.

'I'll show you,' offered Tessa, rising with her. 'Those seats are reserved,' she declared to the company at large. 'No pinching them while we're gone.'

Erin felt Nick's eyes on her, but she couldn't bring herself to look at him for fear of what he might see in her face. Jealousy was a soul-destroying emotion.

Tessa led the way back indoors and out through the far side of the lounge, answering all greetings on the way with a smile and a promise to make the rounds in a little while. The corridor beyond had doors opening off it from both sides. Choosing one, she ushered Erin through into a luxuriously furnished bedroom.

'There's an *en suite* if you really need it,' she said. 'I got the feeling that you just wanted out for a few minutes.' She paused, viewing the younger face shrewdly. 'If you're half the girl I think you are, you won't let that *femme fatale* out there put you off. If your Nick is half the man I think *he* is, he can see right through her anyway.'

Too downcast to even try dissembling, Erin lifted her shoulders. 'Does it make a difference?'

'Of course it makes a difference. Men being the way they are, they're likely to be physically stirred by someone like Dione, but if they've any sense at all, that's as far as it goes.'

Erin looked at the older woman curiously. 'I gather you don't like her very much.'

'You gather rightly. Dione's a predator. She feeds on male attention. She even tried it on with Bryn when we were here last year.' Tessa gave a short laugh. 'He found it amusing. I was more inclined towards murder. It would be great to see her deposed! What's more,' she added, 'I think you're the one to do it.'

'I wish I could share your confidence,' returned Erin on a doubtful note. 'I just don't have the same pulling power.'

'Don't be so self-deprecating.' Tessa took her by the shoulders and turned her about to face the full-length wall mirror. 'Just look at yourself! You've got everything it takes to have Nick eating out of your hand! If you want him, fight for him! Show Dione he's taken!'

Looking from her own reflection to the zealous green eyes of the woman at her back, Erin felt her mettle beginning to firm again. If Nick was worth having he *had* to be worth fighting for, regardless of the odds!

'Attagirl!' encouraged Tessa, registering the change of expression. 'Get back out there and give 'em what for!'

Nick was still talking with Bryn when they got outside again. Refusing to allow herself time for reflection, Erin put a proprietary hand on his arm, smiling up at the older man.

'You won't mind if I steal him away to dance? They're playing our favourite tune.'

If Bryn was taken aback he didn't show it. 'Not at all,' he assured her. 'In fact we might join you.' He glanced his wife's way. 'Feel like dancing?'

'Such finesse!' she sighed, and he grinned.

'Take it or leave it.'

Face unrevealing, Nick slid a hand about Erin's narrow waist to guide her around the intervening groups to the cleared area where several couples already gyrated to the piped music. Reaching it, she moved directly into his arms, sliding both hands over his shoulders to lock her fingers loosely together at his nape and look up into the ironic grey eyes.

'Since when did we have a favourite tune?' he asked.

'Since now,' she said. 'You obviously weren't going to ask me to dance, so I decided to take matters into my own hands.'

'With a vengeance,' he agreed drily. 'What makes you so sure I didn't have it in mind to ask you anyway?'

'Because if you'd asked anyone it was probably going to be Dione, and she's the one I don't intend to let near you.'

His mouth took on a slant. 'Is that a fact?'

'Yes,' she said firmly, determined not to give way to any undermining doubts. 'She doesn't have the same claim on you that I do.'

'And what exactly is that?'

'You're *my* first.' She paused, holding his gaze, heart

fluttering like a trapped bird. 'I don't want anyone else making love to me—ever.'

'Thinking of joining a convent?'

Erin shook her head. 'You know what I'm saying. I want to be married to you. I want to have your children. I want—'

'Whoa!' Nick sounded less than amused. 'I thought you weren't interested in marriage?'

'I lied. Of course I'm interested. You might not love me the way I love you yet, but you will. I'm going to make sure of it. I'll even let you paint me in the nude if you want to. After all, you wouldn't be seeing anything you haven't already seen.'

'That's enough,' he said on a brusque note. 'Joke over!'

'Who's joking?' She pressed herself closer to him as they moved, elated to see the sudden spark leap in his eyes. 'I want you, Nick. And you want me. *Don't* you?'

'One more word, and I'm taking you home!' he threatened.

'Great!' she said. 'That means we can be alone.'

The hands at her back were hard. 'Stop it,' he gritted. 'Now!'

'Or you'll do what?' she queried, too far along the line to consider backing down. 'Spank me?'

Humour fought a brief and losing battle with anger in the lean features. Reaching up, he took hold of her hands and dragged them down from about his neck, pressing her far enough away to clear a limited space between them.

'I said cut it out!' he clipped. 'I don't know what's got into you, but—'

He broke off as she hoisted an eyebrow in faithful imitation, letting out his breath with explosive force. Turned about and propelled ahead of him off the floor, Erin kept a smile on her lips for the benefit of those about them, even now rejecting any inclination towards withdrawal. Perseverance paid in the end. She clung to that thought.

Nick made no attempt to steer her indoors, making instead for the shelter of the trees edging the beach. He came to a stop in the shadow of a coconut palm growing obliquely across their path, his face hard set in the filtered moonlight.

'Whatever game you think you're playing, it stops right here!'

'It's no game,' she said steadfastly. 'I love you, Nick. If you'd let yourself, you could love me too. You're halfway to it already.'

'Because I made love to you?' There was cynicism in the tilt of his lip. 'It's only the very naive who see the two as synonymous.'

Blue eyes refused to flicker away. 'So I'm naive. Preferable to being over-practised. Dione will let you down sooner or later. I wouldn't. That has to make me the better proposition when it comes to taking a wife.'

Nick gave a short laugh. 'It might, if a wife was what I was looking for.' He studied her pure young features, cynicism increasing as his eyes followed the smooth line of her throat to linger for a timeless moment on the tender curve of her breasts. 'I was weak enough to let myself be overcome by a lovely face and body, but there's no way I'd consider marrying you.'

'Even if I turned out to be pregnant?' she asked softly.

The grey eyes narrowed. 'Are you trying to tell me something?'

Erin shook her head again, wondering at her ability to stay calm and collected in such circumstances. 'It's too soon to know one way or the other. And you didn't answer the question. Would you marry me if I was having your baby?'

There was a pause, an expression she couldn't decipher

in his eyes. 'It would have to make a difference,' he conceded.

'Then I hope I am!'

Anger flared once more, tautening the lean features into
a grim mask. 'The last thing you need is to be tied down
with a baby at your age!'

'What does age have to do with it?' she demanded.
'What does age have to do with anything? Did you ever
see a better suited couple than Tessa and Bryn?'

Nick eyed her in dawning realisation. 'She put you up
to this, didn't she? Just what did you tell her?'

'I didn't tell her anything,' Erin denied, aware even as
she said it how unlikely it was that he'd believe it. 'She
guessed how things were.'

'Oh, sure! One look at the two of us and she had the
whole picture!' He spoke with a clipped quietness more
telling than if he'd ranted and raved. 'I can't really complain, can I? If I hadn't—' He broke off, lips compressing.
'That's enough!'

Erin shot a hand out to grasp his arm as he started to
turn away, pulling him back round to face her with a
strength that surprised them both. 'It isn't enough,' she said
forcefully. 'Not nearly!'

Sliding both arms about his shoulders, she put passionate
lips to his, willing him to respond, for his arms to enclose
her, moulding her to the hard angles of his body. For a
brief moment it seemed as if he might do just that as his
mouth softened a fraction and began to answer, his hands
sliding down her back to draw her closer the way he had
done in the pool that night. The deprivation when he suddenly and roughly jerked her away from him was all the
more brutal for that delay.

'It isn't going to happen,' he gritted.

This time there was no stopping him as he turned back
the way they had come—no breaking the grip he had on

her upper arm. Erin went along because she had no choice, but she wasn't beaten yet, she vowed. Tessa had sown too strong a seed.

Dione happened to be looking their way when they emerged from the shadow of the trees. The look that crossed her face gladdened Erin's heart. If nothing else, she had shown the woman that Nick wasn't her exclusive property.

The youngest by a couple of years at least, Samantha was over in a corner of the patio with a small group. Nick steered Erin over to them and left it to Tim to introduce her to his brother Harley.

'I've been waiting to meet you,' said the latter with a keenness that might have been flattering if she hadn't had her sights set on other goals. 'Mother said you were pretty, but I didn't realise just *how* pretty!'

Tim gave a derisive snort. 'How corny can you get!'

'Let's leave the children to play,' suggested his brother, not a whit put out. 'It's impossible to hold an intelligent conversation with this lot.'

'Thanks!' exclaimed Samantha indignantly, and received a condescending smile.

'Excluding newcomers, perhaps. I'll leave it to you to teach them some English manners.'

'I wouldn't rely on it,' said Erin jokingly as he drew her away from the group. 'There are times when my sister forgets all she ever knew about good behaviour.'

'She's in bad company with Tim, then. Father despairs of him doing anything worthwhile with his life.'

'He's only seventeen,' Erin defended, sorry now for having made the remark. 'There's plenty of time for him to make good.'

'Not while he spends nearly as much time out of school as in it. Being buddy-buddy with Reece Brady doesn't help. His folks have no control at all.' He made a dismissive gesture. 'Anyway, that's enough on *that* subject. I'm far more interested in you. Where have you been all my life?'

Tim had a point, Erin reflected, keeping a straight face with an effort. 'Growing up, I suppose,' she said.

Harley laughed. 'Very smart! I like a woman with a quick wit! Shall we dance?'

About to refuse, Erin spotted Nick taking to the floor with Dione, and abruptly changed her mind. 'I'd love to.'

'The music's a bit dated, I'm afraid,' he apologised, providing unnecessary guidance via a hand at her back. 'Father's a sixties fan.'

'I quite like that era too,' Erin returned lightly. 'You look a lot like your father. You and Tim both.'

'And he looks very much like Grandfather. It's a strong male line. Dione, of course, takes after Mother.'

It hardly took a degree in genetics to work that one out, thought Erin drily. Harley might be both closer to her own age and extremely good-looking, but he left her totally unmoved. After Nick, she would never be satisfied with her peers.

Except that there wasn't going to be any 'after Nick' she reminded herself, reinforcing her purpose. Whatever it took, they were going to be together.

She caught his eye over Dione's shoulder as Harley urged her ahead of him onto the floor, directing a challenging gaze that met with little response. He could chill her out all he liked; it wasn't going to work.

'Shirley obviously isn't your real grandmother,' she said when she and Harley were moving in slow unison to the music, unable to come up with any more riveting conversational gambit.

'No,' he confirmed. 'She and Grandfather were married the week before Bryn and Tessa. This was their house then, but they moved to a smaller place up the coast when Father and Mother married.'

'Do you see much of them? Bryn and Tessa, I mean?'

'I dare say we might see more of them now they're going to be here full time. He's much older than she is, of course.'

'Twelve years isn't much!' said Erin, a little too emphatically, and drew a surprised glance.

'It's a great deal more of a gap than I'd want myself. I think four is just about right.'

'You're looking for someone around your sister's age, then?'

Harley gave a laugh. 'As I said, a woman of wit! You and I are going to be spending a lot of time together from now on, Erin.'

It was the sheer assumption that riled her the most. Putting him down was uppermost in her mind at that moment, the consequences ignored. 'I don't see Nick allowing it once we're married,' she returned. 'He's very possessive.'

In any other circumstances Harley's expression would have made her want to laugh. 'Dropped on from a great height' was the nearest description.

'He's your uncle, for God's sake!' he spluttered.

'No, he isn't. Sam and I are only half-sisters.' Erin kept her voice steady by sheer force of will, aware of having gone too far, and seeing no way out. She made an attempt all the same. 'This is just between the two of us, Harley. We don't want it broadcasting around yet.'

'I'll bet *he* doesn't!' Harley sounded savage. 'He should be ashamed of himself, taking advantage of a girl half his age!'

'Why should age make a difference?' Erin protested. 'It didn't with Tessa and Bryn.'

'Not to them, maybe. Nobody else approved.'

'How would you know that? You weren't even born when they married!'

'My father was. He'd already—' Harley caught himself

up, obviously regretting what he had been about to say. 'That's all in the past. We're talking about you and that...*artist*!' The amount of invective he managed to get into the word gave it a whole new connotation. 'I suppose he talked you into posing for him in the nude—the way he did Dione. The man's a pervert!'

There were only three couples left on the dance floor at present, neither of the other two close enough to overhear what was being said—especially with Harley gritting everything through his teeth. It had to be obvious to anyone looking their way that something was wrong, though, thought Erin, not caring to glance in Nick's direction.

The very idea of his painting Dione in the nude set her own teeth on edge. She had a vivid image of those voluptuous curves reclining on the chaise longue in the studio—of Nick putting down his brush to go to take the woman in his arms. Taking what Tessa had said into consideration, Dione would probably know every trick in the book when it came to pleasuring a man—unlike herself, who could only rely on instinct. Her virginity had been her only real asset. Without it, what did she have to offer?

'I think I'd like to sit down,' she said huskily.

Harley made no attempt to dissuade her. He was probably coming to the conclusion that she deserved all she got, Erin reflected.

'I hope I can rely on you to forget what I told you,' she said as they moved away from the dance floor, without much hope at all. 'It's really no one else's business anyway.'

There was no verbal reply, just a shrug that could mean anything, followed by an abrupt departure. Tessa was beckoning, the chair at her side still empty. Erin made her way over to slide into it with a wry grimace in response to the questioning look.

'I've just done something very stupid,' she admitted. 'I told Harley Nick and I are going to be married.'

Comprehension was immediate. 'A chat-up stopper if ever I heard one! I take it Nick hasn't actually asked you as yet?'

'No.' Erin paused. 'I asked Harley to keep it to himself. Do you think he might?'

'Doubtful, I'm afraid. He'll have had his nose put out of joint. That isn't going to go down too well. He's used to having girls falling over themselves.' Tessa gave a dry little smile. 'A chip off the old block! His father found it hard to take when *I* turned *him* down.'

'So I gathered.' Erin glanced over to where Bryn stood talking with another couple of men. 'Was there much opposition?'

'Not so much opposition as lack of appreciation in some quarters. ''Autumn weds spring'' was how one idiot put it, which was totally ridiculous; Bryn was only thirty-one. And, no, I don't consider another few years of any consequence. You'll find you grow closer in every sense of the word.'

Erin found a weak smile. 'Providing I ever get the chance.'

'It's too late to start backing out now. You're going to have to see it through.' The green eyes were encouraging. 'It will work out, just see if it doesn't. Nick will be the envy of every able-bodied man on the island when news gets around.'

If Harley's reaction was anything to go by, he'd as likely be vilified, Erin reflected ruefully. How could she have been so utterly irresponsible?

It soon became apparent from the glances cast her way that Harley had lost little time in spreading the tidings. Nick had disappeared, as had Dione—whether together or not there was no telling. With neither courage nor desire to go and help herself from the vast buffet supper laid out under the loggia, Erin picked without appetite at the plateful Tessa brought back for her, wondering how long it was going to take for word to reach Nick's ears. If he was with Dione in private somewhere, it could be quite some time.

Bryn asked her to dance when the music started up again. Held loosely in his arms, Erin thought again how like Nick he was in many ways. Not so much in actual looks, perhaps, but in his unequivocal masculinity, his ability to assert without arrogance. She could well understand why Tessa had fallen in love with him all those years ago—why she was so obviously crazy about him still.

'I believe congratulations are in order,' he proffered. 'Although I should really be saying that to Nick, of course.'

Erin gave a small resigned sigh, seeing no point in trying to keep up the pretence when Tessa was already in possession of the true state of affairs. 'I'd rather you didn't say anything to Nick. It's all a mistake.'

'I had an idea it might be.' He paused, looking down at her with quizzical expression. 'These things have a way of getting out of hand. Especially with help from my wife.'

'It doesn't have anything to do with Tessa,' Erin denied quickly.

He smiled. 'I'd very much doubt that. The two of you have had your heads together since you got here. Tessa remembers the difficulties we went through ourselves by not being forthright with each other. It would be like her to try giving your situation a helping hand.'

'There is no situation.'

'No? That wasn't the impression I had when Nick towed you off the floor a while back. He looked like a man with quite a lot on his mind.'

'Still has,' said a grim voice. 'You'll excuse me if I cut in?'

'Sure.' Bryn yielded his hold and moved unhurriedly

away, leaving Erin to face a pair of steely eyes. With two ways to go, she opted for the boldest, chin lifting.

'So?'

Nick drew her to him, holding her in a crushing grip as he started to move in time to the music. She could feel the tension in him: a coiled spring held in check by sheer willpower.

'Just what did you hope to achieve?' he clipped. 'Did you really think I'd be so overwhelmed with shame I'd feel forced into marrying you?'

Erin stiffened her backbone, adopting a taunting tone she knew was asking for trouble, and suddenly not giving a damn. 'Smile, darling, or people are going to think we're having a row already!'

She hadn't thought it possible for his arms to tighten their hold on her any further, but they did, shortening her breath as her breasts came up hard against his chest. 'People are going to think a hell of a lot worse if you keep this up!' he threatened.

'I told you how I feel about you,' she said, ignoring the injunction. 'If Mohammed won't come to the mountain, then the mountain has to shift for itself. I was a virgin before you. Marriage is the price you have to pay for the privilege.'

Nick was silent for a lengthy moment, anger giving way to some other less easily identifiable emotion as he studied her upturned face. 'I can't believe this is you talking,' he said at last.

Erin could hardly believe it either. The words just kept coming. 'I love you,' she said, and kissed him on the lips. 'There's nothing you can say that's going to alter that. If you marry me I'll be the best wife any man ever had! I'll wash your shirts, darn your socks, cook all your favourite meals!'

An unwilling smile touched the corners of his mouth. 'I

don't need any socks darning, and Bella does everything else.'

'Not *every*thing.' Erin softened her voice, drawing on some hitherto untried feminine artifice. 'I'd be there whenever you wanted me, Nick—for whatever you wanted. I'd love and honour you—even obey!'

He gave a dry laugh. 'Don't let's get too carried away!'

'I mean it!' Right then she would have promised him anything. 'You can't marry Dione! I won't let you!'

'I never had any intention of marrying Dione,' he said with convincing certitude. 'I'd no intention of marrying anyone.'

Erin seized on the past tense implication. 'That was before we met. I knew the first minute I clapped eyes on you that no mere boy would ever be able to make me feel what you made me feel. I hardly slept a wink that night for thinking about you.'

The smile came again, tinged with more than a little irony. 'Ditto—though I'd doubt that we were thinking along quite the same lines.'

'Don't be too sure. I might not have had the experience back then, but I had all the feelings.' She paused, searching the lean features. 'Did you really feel that way about me even then?'

'I'd have had to be made from stone not to. You were—' He broke off, jaw hardening again. 'I should never have brought you back here with me.'

'I'd have died an old maid if you'd left me behind.'

'No, you wouldn't. You'd have met someone—'

'If you're going to say someone nearer my own age, don't!' she cut in. 'They're boring. Take Harley. He's so full of himself he thinks his company alone is enough to make a girl happy!'

'It would be with most.'

'Why? Because he's a good catch?'

'One of the island's finest.'

'Well, whoever he finishes up with, they're welcome to him. All *I* want is *you*!'

Nick gave a long drawn sigh, anger no longer a factor. 'You might think you do now.'

'I don't think; I know.' Having got this far, Erin wasn't about to give ground. His arms had loosened their hold on her; she closed the slight space between them again, relishing the movement of his thigh muscles against her—there was a lot to be said for high heels when a man was so much taller. 'Whatever arguments you come up with, you're not going to change anything,' she whispered against his cheek. 'I love you!'

He was silent for a lengthy moment, though he made no attempt to put her from him. When he did finally speak he sounded resigned. 'We'd better make it known you're not really my niece.'

Heart leaping, Erin drew back her head to search his face, not finding quite the confirmation she sought. 'I already told Harley I'm not.'

'That will have to do for now.'

'For now?' Her spirits had plummeted again.

The grey eyes offered no comfort. 'Short of forcing you to make a public retraction, I don't have much choice. In a few weeks' time—providing nothing else occurs—we can call the whole thing off. Until then, you don't say anything to anyone. Is that clear?'

The music had come to a stop, Erin realised. People were moving off the floor. Those who hadn't already heard the news would soon be put in the picture, only it still wasn't going to be for real.

'I think we'll call it a day,' Nick said firmly, turning her about. 'It's gone midnight.'

Erin was too downcast to even think of resisting. Catching Tessa's eye across the patio, she summoned a smile, reluctant to show her defeat. It was obvious from the way people were looking at the two of them that the rumour had gone all the way round. Obvious too, as Nick led her towards the house, that he had no intention of taking the least notice.

They were almost there when Dione put in an appearance, ignoring others in the vicinity, including Erin herself, her face a study as she confronted the man she had believed was hers.

'Is it true?' she demanded.

'That depends,' Nick said levelly, 'on what you've heard.'

'Harley just told me you're planning on marrying your niece!'

'There's no blood relationship. Erin and Samantha are half-sisters. He was already informed of that. Is your mother inside?' he added. 'I'd like to thank her for the hospitality before we go.'

'You can't be serious!' Like her brother, Dione found rejection impossible to accept. 'She's just a...kid!'

'*She* is more than old enough to speak for herself!' Erin cut in before Nick could answer, losing sight of everything he'd said in the searing heat of the moment. 'Wedding invitations will be in the post shortly.'

There was a laugh from somewhere behind them; probably Tessa enjoying the younger woman's comeuppance, thought Erin fleetingly. Mouth set like a trap, eyes sending out lightning bolts, Dione stepped aside to let them pass as Nick urged her forward with an ungentle hand at her back.

Erin could feel the anger in him, but she couldn't find it in herself to regret what she'd just done. It was time everyone—including Nick himself—realised she was no wilting violet ready to accept anything thrown at her. The fight wasn't over yet by a long chalk!

CHAPTER EIGHT

PAMELA made no effort to conceal her feelings when they took their leave of her.

'You could at least have told Dione what was going on in private, instead of leaving her to find out this way!' she berated.

'That was my fault,' Erin claimed swiftly. 'I let it slip to Harley. I did ask him not to spread it around.'

'That's hardly the point.' Pamela was giving no quarter, her anger directed at Nick. 'You should be ashamed of yourself!'

'You're probably right,' he agreed without expression.

Samantha barely waited till they got outside before letting fly with her own indignant reproofs.

'You're a real pair of dark horses! Why didn't you tell me what was going on? I felt an absolute idiot back there!'

'Don't exaggerate,' Nick said shortly.

Erin slid into the front passenger seat when he opened the car door for her, avoiding looking at him directly. That there were going to be ructions over that scene with Dione there was no doubt. She had put him in a cleft-stick, with no way out other than to show her up for the liar she was. Most men, she had to admit, would probably have done exactly that.

'So aren't you going to say anything about it at all?' demanded Samantha plaintively, after five minutes during which no one spoke.

'Such as what?' asked Nick.

'Such as when you came up with the idea in the first

118

place. Rin was making out she didn't even fancy you this afternoon!'

'I wasn't ready to talk about it then,' Erin claimed.

'You'd only just met Harley, but you were ready enough to tell *him*!'

'That was...unintentional.'

'Hooey! He said you couldn't wait to tell him!'

Out of the corner of her eye, Erin saw Nick's hand tauten on the wheel. 'It wasn't at all like that,' she denied.

'So how else was it?'

'Let it drop.' Nick spoke quietly enough but the under-tone brooked no debate. 'You'll be told what you need to know when you need to know it.'

Affronted, Samantha thumped back in her seat. 'Pardon me for breathing!' she muttered.

Nick ignored the comment. Glancing sideways at the im-passive profile, Erin rallied her flagging spirits. There was to be no backing down, out, or in any other direction. If she wanted him, it had to be an all-in effort.

Reaching the house, he bade the two of them to go on indoors while he put the car away. Still sulking, Samantha made no answer when Erin wished her goodnight, swishing off up the stairs without a backward glance. Erin sat down on the bottom step to wait. Tomorrow might be another day, but tonight was the time to get things sorted.

Nick looked unsurprised to see her there when he came in. 'We'll go to the library,' he said curtly.

The lovely book-lined room where Erin had spent many enjoyable hours was at the side of the house farthest away from the bedrooms in use—although it was doubtful, she thought, that Sam would have heard anything even if she had been directly overhead.

'I know what you're going to say,' she started in as Nick closed the door, 'but I couldn't help it.'

'Yes, you could,' he retorted. 'You thoroughly enjoyed shoving it down Dione's throat!'

'I was entitled to resent being treated like some trashy kid!' she declared. 'All right, so I enjoyed it. She obviously thought she owned you!'

'Maybe she had some reason.'

Erin drew in a lip, by no means deaf to the nuances. 'However many times you've slept with her, it doesn't give her any rights over you. You said you'd never had any intention of marrying her.'

'True.'

'So she was sticking her neck out going for you the way she did—which means you should have chopped her down to size yourself instead of leaving me to do it for you.'

Still not moving away from the door, Nick eyed her contemplatively. 'Dione isn't the only one in need of chopping down to size!'

Erin took fresh heart from the hint of humour in the line of his mouth, faint though it was. 'As the woman you're going to marry, I've every right to be uppity. Yes, I know what you told me; it doesn't mean I have to accept it.'

'What other course did you have in mind?'

She drew a steadying breath. 'Everyone believes we're going to be married. If you try to wriggle out of it now I'll sue for breach of promise!'

'I'll make sure to hire a good lawyer.'

'I mean it, Nick!' Erin put all the certitude she was capable of into that statement. 'I'm *not* giving up!'

There was a pause, an expression she couldn't be sure of in the grey eyes. 'It wouldn't work.'

'Yes, it would!' She was eager, sensing a certain weakening. 'I might not be experienced, but I can learn to be everything you need. All you have to do is show me.'

'There's more to marriage than sex.' His voice had gained a rough edge again. 'I'd be doing you no favour in marrying you, Erin. You're infatuated with the idea of it, that's all.'

'Not true. I know the difference between love and infatuation.'

'Of course you do.'

The satire lit flares in the blue eyes. 'If it was just infatuation, I'd be turned off by that kind of thing for a start! You can be a real pain at times.'

'That makes two of us,' he returned drily. 'Hardly a recipe for a harmonious marriage.'

'Total harmony would be downright boring,' she retorted. 'There's nothing like a good row for getting the adrenalin flowing!'

Nick looked as if he were fighting to stay on top of a situation fast getting out of hand. 'Where did you hear that bit of philosophy?'

'I probably read it somewhere,' she admitted, 'but it's true enough. Married couples who claim they've never had a single row must either be lying their heads off or too bovine to make the effort. Just imagine missing out on the making up afterwards.'

There was no controlling the laugh this time. 'You paint an alluring picture!'

'Private sale only,' she flashed back. 'You're going to say yes in the end, Nick, so why not save a lot of time and trouble and say it now? I'll be—'

'I know—the best wife a man ever had.' He studied her standing there, piled hair gleaming under the overhead light, shoulders bared in the blue dress, legs long and slender beneath the softly draped skirt, his lips twisting. 'I'd have to reserve judgement on that.'

Erin hesitated no longer, unable to control the urgent need to be close to him. Nick slid his arms about her supple young body as she raised an eager mouth, the look of a man driven beyond endurance in his eyes. The kiss was everything she'd hoped for. She savoured every moment of it, loving the taste of him, the scent of him, the overwhelming contact with that lean hard body.

'You wouldn't regret it,' she murmured against his lips. 'You wouldn't *ever* regret it!'

'You'd better get to bed,' he said, putting her gently away from him. He shook his head at the look on her face, his expression resolute again. 'Sleep on it. You'll probably feel differently in the morning.'

She could sleep on it from here to Christmas without it making a scrap of difference, Erin could have told him, but she had a better idea.

'All right,' she agreed, feigning resignation. 'Are you coming up?'

'I'm in need of a cooling-off period,' he said with a certain irony. 'You've got me so I'm not sure whether I'm standing on my head or my heels!'

Erin doubted it. She might have undermined his resistance but she'd by no means fully conquered it as yet. That was something she had to work on.

She went upstairs quietly, passing her own bedroom to slip into his, and standing at the doorway for a moment to calm herself before crossing to switch on a single bedside lamp.

She was wearing nothing but a pair of lace panties beneath the blue dress. Leaving both garments where they fell, she slid between the crisp cotton sheets, recalling with shuddering anticipation the last time she had done this. Nick wasn't going to kick her out tonight—or any other night, if it came to that. So far as she was concerned, they were married already. The wedding was merely trimming.

It seemed an age before he came up. She had turned out the lamp again, and he didn't bother to put on a light. The moon had either gone down or out, leaving the bed in deep shadow. Erin listened to the sound of his movements, hoping he wasn't planning on taking a shower. She wanted his lovemaking so badly she could barely contain herself.

The butterflies in her stomach increased their fluttering tenfold on his approach to the bed. He saw her only when he was a couple of feet away, coming to an abrupt halt.

'This wasn't what I meant by sleeping on it,' he said.

'It's my interpretation,' she claimed, senses clamouring on sight of his naked outline. 'We're not going to argue over a definition, are we?'

With eyes grown accustomed to the darkness, it was possible to see the struggle going on as he stood there looking at her. Erin threw off the sheet and held out her arms invitingly, willing him to give in, to stop thinking about possible future problems and do what he so obviously wanted to do right now. She didn't care *how* she got him, only that she did get him. Her life was worth nothing without him.

His move to open the top drawer in the bedside cabinet took her by surprise for a moment, until she realised what it was he was after. She didn't care about that aspect either, but if it made him feel safer then so be it.

She welcomed the impact of his body as he came down over her. The touch of his lips at her breast was agony and ecstasy rolled into one, his tongue searing a path around her areola, the potent weight pressuring her thighs apart. She wrapped her legs about him, too hungry for the tumultuous fulfilment she knew was to come to wait a moment longer for the sensation of him inside her. All man, and all hers—and woe betide *anyone* who tried to take him away from her!

Like that other morning, she woke up in her own bed, only this time it was in the safe and sure knowledge of even better things to come. She hadn't wanted to leave Nick at all, but he had insisted. Until they were married, they continued to occupy separate rooms, he'd said. Erin really couldn't see what difference it made now.

Mrs Nicholas Carson. It sounded so impressive. There was no reason to wait any longer than absolutely necessary for the wedding. After what she'd said to Dione, everyone would be expecting it to be soon, anyway. Lying there, luxuriating in the thought of it all, she even found an element of sympathy for the older woman. Losing any man to another woman would be hard enough for someone like Dione to take; losing Nick was obviously beyond all reckoning.

The tentative knock on the door brought her starting upright in anticipation, until common sense pointed out the unlikelihood of it being Nick out there—a guess confirmed when the door slowly opened to reveal Samantha's face peering round it.

'I thought you might have company,' she said, coming all the way in. She closed the door and rested her back against it, viewing her sister's tumbled hair with open speculation. 'I suppose he went back to his own room.'

'He never left it,' said Erin truthfully. She hesitated, not at all sure how best to approach the subject. 'I'm sorry you had to learn what you did the way you did,' was the best she could come up with. 'It's just the way it happened.'

Samantha looked sceptical. 'The way you planned it, you mean. Was it my saying how Dad blackmailed you into giving up school that gave you the idea?'

'I didn't *blackmail* Nick!' Erin denied hotly.

'Near enough, letting Harley spread it around like that. It would take somebody even harder than Nick can be to force you to stand up in front of all those people and admit to making it up.'

There was too much truth in what she was saying for comfort, Erin acknowledged wryly—rallying her spirits with the thought that she had only hastened the inevitable. Nick wouldn't have agreed to marry her if he hadn't had the idea in mind himself—even if only tentatively.

'I love him,' she said. 'He's the best thing that ever happened to me.'

'You never had a proper boyfriend to compare with,' the girl protested. 'Why don't you go for someone like Harley Wyman?'

'Even if I could have him I wouldn't want him,' Erin assured her. 'Or anyone else, for that matter. Nick is everything I could ever look for.'

'But he's old! *And* he's my uncle. If you marry him, he'll be my brother-in-law too. Have you thought about that?'

Erin hadn't. She found the notion quite intriguing. 'I suppose I'll be your aunt as well as your sister,' she mused. 'Quite a tangle!'

'The whole thing's disgusting!' Samantha burst out. 'You've got to stop it, Rin!'

Erin bit her lip, hardly knowing what to say. 'You didn't seem to think it so disgusting yesterday when you were teasing me about wanting to go to bed with him,' she appealed.

'That was just talk. You know it was! And it's not just my opinion either. You should have heard some of the comments last night!'

'I'm not interested in what other people think,' Erin countered. 'Neither is Nick. You didn't meet Tessa and Bryn Marshall, did you? If you had, you'd realise that love knows no barriers.'

'I'll bet you read that somewhere!' Samantha was not to be pacified. 'Don't expect me to be a bridesmaid, that's all! I shan't even come to the wedding!'

Erin sat gazing at the door for several moments after it closed on the departing figure, trying not to allow her sister's disapproval to affect her too deeply. Sam would come round. She had to come round. Nick would talk to her.

He was already seated at the breakfast table when she

went out some half an hour later, though there was no sign of Samantha as yet. Erin slid her arms over the broad shoulders from behind to press a kiss to the upper point of his jaw.

'Good morning, lover!' she laughed.

There was a sudden clatter of crockery as the trolley Bella was pushing towards them along the veranda collided with a potted palm.

'What are you about, girl?' she exclaimed in scandalised tones.

'I'm saying hallo to my fiancé,' Erin answered blithely. 'We're going to be married, Bella. Isn't it terrific?'

From the expression on the wide black face as her glance went from Erin to the man still seated, Bella had other adjectives in mind. 'She's just a child, Mr Nick! What are you thinkin' of?'

'Right at this moment, a cup of strong black coffee,' he returned wryly. 'I didn't intend dropping it on you quite this way, Bella, but it will be all round the island before the day's out, anyway.'

'Be pleased for us,' Erin pleaded. 'We know what we're doing.' She slid round and across Nick's knees, to plant another kiss on none too willing lips, refusing to allow his lack of response to undermine her ebullience. 'Don't we, darling?'

'That's enough,' he said in a low tone.

There was no ignoring the look in the grey eyes. Not anger, exactly, but a long way from ardour for sure. Sobering, Erin transferred to a chair, aware of a very great difference in mood from that of the night before. It was too late to start having doubts again. If they hadn't been committed before, they were now. They had to be!

Bella finished serving up breakfast in disapproving silence, and took herself back to the kitchen. Erin waited until the scarlet-clad back had disappeared around the cor-

ner of the veranda before giving voice to the concerns cir-
cling in her head.

'Have you changed your mind?' she asked.

'No,' Nick answered with reassuring promptitude. 'I'd
just prefer you to keep your feet on the ground.'

'All the time?' she queried innocently, and saw his
mouth start to crease at the corners.

'In public, at any rate. We're going to be running into a
whole lot of reactions like Bella's.'

Samantha's, for one, she could have told him. She hoped
her sister would have had second thoughts by the time she
put in an appearance.

'It's ridiculous!' she exclaimed. 'You'd think there were
fifty years between us! Not that it would make any difference if there were,' she added. 'I'd still feel the same way
about you.'

'At sixty-nine, I might have found it difficult keeping up
with you,' he said drily. 'I've a feeling I might anyway.'

'Rubbish!' She could say that with certainty. 'You're as
virile as they come!'

His grin was good to see. 'You wouldn't know how they
come.'

'I can guess.' She was laughing, eyes sparkling with
pure, unadulterated happiness—the latter fading a little as
her eyes went beyond him to where her sister stood framed
in the doorway. 'Sam...'

The younger girl turned abruptly on her heel and van-
ished back inside again. Nick looked round in time to catch
a glimpse of her retreating figure, turning back to direct a
questioning gaze.

'What was that about?'

Erin adopted a flippancy she was far from feeling. 'She's
been mixing with too many Wymans.'

'I see.' It was apparent that he saw all too clearly. 'I was under the impression she was just piqued last night because she hadn't been told in advance.'

'She probably was, to start with. She's had all night to think about it.' Erin hesitated. 'She came in to see me earlier. She said some people had made nasty remarks.'

'As I told you, it's to be expected.' Nick had sobered too. 'I don't personally give a damn, but you might not find it all that easy to handle. It's more than just the age gap. You're my brother's stepdaughter. A lot of people will see it as not all that far removed from incest.'

'Anyone stupid enough to think like that isn't worth bothering about!' she dismissed scathingly. 'At least we can rely on Tessa and Bryn for support. They've been through it themselves.'

Nick refrained from pointing out that they had been far away from island gossip for the most part. Viewing the angular features, Erin felt a nigh on irresistible desire to get up and go to him again—to feel the security of his arms about her, the delicious tingle of his lips against her skin. The last thing she wanted right now was food.

'Did you finish packing the crates yet?' she asked, pouring coffee for them both as a means of taking her mind off her urges.

'I didn't even get started,' he admitted. 'Too many other things on my mind.'

She looked at him through her lashes. 'Me being one of them, I hope.'

'You being all of them.'

'Really?' Erin was highly gratified. 'And what conclusions did you reach about me?'

'That the best thing all round would be to send you to art college back home—providing there were no complications.' The smile held an element of self-mockery. 'I didn't reckon on finding myself engaged to be married before the day was out.'

'But you don't regret it now?' she asked with a trace of anxiety. 'You really do want me?'

Nick eyed the lovely young face, his mouth curving again. 'There isn't a man alive who wouldn't want you.'

It wasn't quite what she'd asked, and was a great deal less than she'd wanted to hear, but it was obviously all she was going to get right now. He hadn't once used the word 'love,' Erin realised, thinking back. Not even last night in the throes of passion, although she must have said it a dozen times or more. According to magazine problem pages, she wasn't alone in finding romantic wordplay in short supply. A man's emotions were far more physically orientated than a woman's.

'I could give you a hand with the packing,' she offered, dismissing the matter for now. 'I'd be very careful.'

'I'd be very grateful,' he said. 'It has to be done today. The carrier's due in the morning. If we finish by lunchtime we can drive over to Bathsheba this afternoon, if you like. You'll find the Atlantic coastline very different.'

Erin hesitated. 'Do you mean all three of us?'

'If Sam wants to come. The way she acted a few minutes ago, I'd say it was doubtful.'

Erin doubted it too. 'Couldn't you have a word with her?' she suggested tentatively.

'Telling her what? I can't alter the factors she's upset about.' Nick shook his head decisively. 'She'll have to come round to it in her own time.'

There was sense in what he was saying, Erin had to concede. Sam wasn't going to be swayed by words. What they had to do was show her how right they were to-gether—how unimportant the years between them were. In the meantime, she would just have to put up with the sit-uation.

She was still missing when the two of them finished breakfast. Over at the studio, Erin concentrated on the job in hand. Each canvas had to be fitted into a protective cover before insertion in the padded crate, two of them so large it took a concerted effort to get them safely secured.

'Do you ever paint to order?' she asked, regretting the lost opportunity this last week to study the works in more detail. 'I mean general subjects?'

'Occasionally,' Nick confirmed. 'The cane cutters was a commission from someone who used to live here and wanted a reminder. It will go up for exhibition along with the rest, but with a ''Sold'' sticker already attached. Not a bad incentive.'

'From what Miles said, the public don't need any incentive.' She added lightly, 'Tessa thought Bryn was asking you if you'd do a portrait of her to hang at Bay Marris now that they're here for good.'

'That's right, he did.'

'Are you going to do it?'

'Why not? She'd be an interesting subject.' Nick gave her an oblique glance. 'You in thirty years' time, maybe?'

'Tessa's only forty-six,' Erin corrected pedantically, drawing a grin.

'I'll make a note of that. You never know when it might come up in conversation.'

He was sealing up the last crate, his back half turned to her. Erin allowed her eyes to drift the length of his body, lingering on the firm hemispheres in mounting excitation. Giving way to an ungovernable urge, she moved in behind him to slide both arms about his waist, leaning her cheek against his shirt.

'I want you,' she said softly.

Nick grasped her exploring hand before it could reach its target, the smile there in his voice. 'Behave yourself, or I'll put you across my knee!'

'Whatever turns you on,' she murmured, giving vent to

a squeal as he swung to sweep her up off the floor with an unholy glint in his eye. 'Pax!'

'You,' he said, 'are going to have to learn to wait till you're asked!'

She widened her eyes at him. 'So ask me.'

The glint became a gleam, but only for a moment, damped down by an iron will. 'Not here.'

'Why?' she pressured. 'There's no one likely to turn up unexpectedly, is there?'

'It isn't unknown.' He deposited her back on the ground. 'Not that I don't appreciate the enthusiasm.'

Erin looked at him uncertainly, sensing a subtle alteration in mood. 'It isn't *just* sex I want you for,' she said, trying to make a joke of it. 'It's just that you're so good at it.'

'I do my best.' He was smiling still, but the amusement was definitely edged. 'I need to fetch some more tape. You might start tidying up the debris while I'm gone.'

She watched him go, wondering disconsolately what more he wanted from her. She'd told him time and time again how she felt about him. Surely he could see that sex was only a part of the attraction?

A very good part, admittedly, but not the be-all and end-all.

He hadn't returned by the time she'd finished clearing away the packing remnants. The New York consignment had left a number of the racks empty, but there were still some occupied.

Erin went over to leaf through a stack, pausing in particular admiration of a study of Bella in her red dress. Nick had caught the Bajan woman in an unusually pensive mood, her attention concentrated on the sprays of frangipani she was arranging in one of the big floor vases. Unposed almost certainly, so probably fleshed out from a snatched sketch— and obviously never intended for sale.

Exposing the next canvas in the rack, she came to a

stomach-churning halt, knowing in her heart of hearts that this was what she had really been looking for. Dione reclined, as anticipated, on the chaise longue, one arm draped elegantly over the cushioned end, the other resting along her thigh, a sultry half-smile on her face. She had a superb body, Erin had to acknowledge, full-breasted and hipped, with a waist almost as slender as her own. Her legs maybe weren't quite as long, but that was small consolation. What mattered was that Nick had put the portrait with those he apparently regarded as special.

But then it was, of course. The woman had been his lover. For all she knew he had other similar studies stashed away—a regular pictorial diary, in fact.

If he had, she didn't want to know about it, Erin told herself staunchly. She was going to be his wife. That was more than anyone else had achieved. One thing she wouldn't be doing was allowing him to paint her in the nude, though. After seeing this, she would feel totally inadequate.

CHAPTER NINE

POUNDED by huge Atlantic rollers, the eastern coastline was spectacular. Nick did some lightning sketches of the surfers, and one of Erin herself absorbed in watching them, her hair tossed by the wind.

'Sneaky!' she commented on seeing it. 'I didn't even realise!'

'I didn't want you to,' he said. 'You don't belong in any studio pose. I realised that last week. Too much like trying to capture a cat on a hot tin roof!'

'Frustration,' she returned flippantly. 'You were still playing hard to get.'

Nick gave a dry smile. 'Amazing what a little moonlight can do.' He eyed her consideringly. 'Did you know I was back when you decided to go in the pool that night?'

'No,' she said. 'I hadn't heard the car. I'd torn my one and only suit earlier, that's why I wasn't wearing anything. I thought you were an illusion.'

'One I lost little time in dispelling.'

'You only did what I wanted you to do, so stop castigating yourself!' Erin admonished, and saw his lips widen.

'I'll make every effort. Why don't you show me what you can do while we're sitting here?'

He was offering her the sketchpad and pencil, the glint in his eyes daring her to come up with any saucy retort. Erin took them from him with reluctance.

'I'm very amateur.'

'A gifted one, if Sam's to be believed. Just draw what you see.'

Blue eyes acquired a sudden glint of their own. Holding

the pad so he couldn't see what she was doing, she executed a few swift strokes, finishing off with a scrawled signature across the bottom of the page.

'Portrait of an artist,' she said, handing the pad back.

Nick took one look and burst out laughing. She had done a wicked caricature of him standing before an easel, a huge brush in his hand and a lascivious leer on his lips. She had actually contemplated adding a reclining nude in the background, but decided there was too much risk of his recognising the source of that particular piece of inspiration.

'You,' he said, 'are asking for trouble!' He handed back the pad. 'Let's try for something a little less defamatory.'

She took a great deal longer over the drawing, eyes narrowed against the light, brow furrowed in concentration. Nick stayed silent until she finally handed over the pad with a self-critical little shrug.

'It's not very good. The eyes are wrong.'

She had drawn him again, but in strictly realistic vein this time: a three-quarter facial study showing the strong clean lines. He studied it without comment for several seconds, expression impossible to define.

'You don't have to be kind,' she said at length, unable to stand the suspense. 'I'm not going to fall apart if you tell me it's rubbish.'

'It's a long way removed from being rubbish,' he returned. 'Although I agree with you about the eyes. They're always the most difficult feature to capture. You have talent, for certain. All you need is to work at it. I'll be happy to give you what help I can.'

Erin looked at him suspiciously. 'You're not just saying that?'

'It would be cruel to give you false hopes.' His lips curved. 'It will be an extra facet of interest on honeymoon, if we need it.'

Suspicion melted into sudden entrancement. 'Honeymoon?'

'It comes after most weddings. You might start thinking about where you'd like to spend it—unless you'd rather it was a surprise?'

'Yes. Yes, I would!' Looking at him lounging there on the sand, dark hair tousled, eyes full of dancing amber lights, Erin felt full to overflowing with emotion. 'I must have been born under a lucky star!' she said softly.

She leaned over to kiss him, wishing they were alone. However many times he made love to her, it could never be enough!

It was almost six o'clock when they got back to the house. Bella met them at the door, concern written large on her face. Sam had been missing for the last four hours. The grounds had been searched twice, but there was no sign of her.

'I'll drive around the area in case she went for a walk,' said Nick decisively.

If she had, it wouldn't be just for walking's sake, Erin could have told him. The main road was over a mile away through cane fields not yet cut. If Sam had set out in the hope of hitching a lift down to town, she could quite easily have taken a wrong turning and finished up thoroughly lost. It would be dark before too long. That would vastly reduce the chances of finding her.

'I'll come with you,' she said, trying to curb her anxiety.

They spent half an hour traversing the narrow routes without success. Nick headed for Bridgetown without comment when Erin suggested it on the off chance that Sam had actually made it there, though his expression more than adequately reflected his thoughts. If they did find her down there, she was going to be in serious trouble, Erin gathered. For herself, she only cared about finding her.

With no cruise ships in dock, and most people at supper,

the town was relatively free of tourists. Nick made a slow detour of the main streets, while Erin kept a sharp look-out.

There were plenty of young people around, either gathered in laughing, chattering groups or parading in their Sunday best. Samantha was with one of the former, Tim's arm about shoulders bared by the black boob tube she was wearing, her red skirt so short it only just covered the curve of her behind.

Neither of them items purchased in her company, Erin knew for sure.

Nick drew up at the side of the group, putting a restraining hand on her arm as she made to get out.

'I'll see to it,' he said grimly.

Her back to the road, Samantha was totally unaware of his approach, almost jumping out of the boob tube when he spoke.

'Get in the car,' he ordered. 'And *you'd* better make yourself scarce,' he added to Tim.

'Hey, man, what's all the aggro?' drawled the latter, making no attempt to drop the embrace. 'We're just hangin' out.'

It was obvious that he'd been drinking. Obvious that the girl at his side had too, as she staggered a little in turning to direct an insolent, liner-emphasised blue gaze.

'I'm not coming with *you!*'

Nick wasted no more time on words. Seizing her by the arm, he yanked her out of Tim's grasp and opened the rear door of the car to put her forcibly inside, slamming it closed on her furious protests. Neither Tim nor anyone else in the group moved or made a sound as he strode back round the front to slide behind the wheel, sober enough to recognise a man operating on a dangerously short fuse.

Much as she felt like giving the younger girl a piece of her mind, Erin deemed it wiser to stay mute for the time being and let Nick handle it himself. If Sam had any sense left at all, she would keep her own mouth shut.

Sense, it seemed, was in short supply. Either that, or alcohol was fuelling a false bravado.

'You've no right to do this!' she raged. 'I *hate* you!'

'Keep that up, and you'll have reason to!' Nick said tautly. 'When did you get that damned outfit?'

'When do you think?' came the scathing retort.

'Not when I was with you,' Erin felt moved to cut in. 'Have you been cutting school?'

'So what if I have?'

'You've only been there a week,' Nick snapped. 'What kind of an impression is that supposed to make?'

'It was only one lunchtime.' Samantha was beginning to sound just a little on the defensive side. 'You gave me the chequebook so I could be independent, didn't you?'

'An obvious mistake, if that's the use you're going to put it to!'

There was a lengthy pause while he negotiated the one-way system. When he spoke again it was on a controlled note. 'How did you get down here in the first place?'

'Tim picked me up at the gates.' Samantha rallied to add defiantly, 'Why should *I* have to hang around the house?'

'You didn't have to,' Erin pointed out. 'You could have come to Bathsheba with us.'

'I didn't want to be with you! I still don't! It's horrible!'

'That's enough!' Nick sounded suddenly weary. 'From now on you steer clear of Tim Wyman.'

There was no reply from the rear, but Erin could visualise the mutinous set of her sister's pretty face. Nick was being very forbearing under the circumstances, only Sam wouldn't see it that way.

He bade her go and change her things on reaching the house, refusing to accept her claim not to want any dinner. 'You need something in your stomach to soak up whatever it is you've been drinking,' he stated, viewing her somewhat unsteady progression towards the stairs. 'Just what *have* you had?'

'Can't remember,' she flung back over a shoulder. 'Don't care anyway!'

Erin held her breath, but Nick let it go. 'I could do with a shower myself before we eat,' he said. 'I'll go and tell Bella to hold dinner for another half an hour.'

Mounting the stairs in her sister's wake, Erin fought back the despondency threatening to overtake her. It was no use telling herself she was hardly to blame for Sam's behaviour when it was so obviously a direct result of her own. Nick must be beginning to regret ever having responded to Mr Gordon's call.

There had been no legal obligation. Had he chosen to, he could quite legitimately have washed his hands of the whole affair. Instead, he was now stuck with a forthcoming marriage he hadn't asked for, and a teenager problem most parents would find hard enough to handle.

Feeling very little better after showering, she put on an Indian cotton skirt and sleeveless blouse and went to knock on Sam's door, guessing that in this mood the latter would drag things out to the very last moment.

Opening it when there was no reply, to see her sister sprawled across the bed and apparently fast asleep, she at first didn't believe it. Only when she went right over and heard the heavy breathing did she accept that the sleep was genuine. Not quite a drunken stupor, perhaps, but too close for comfort.

'You're going to spoil everything if you keep this up,' she whispered, pushing the fair hair back from the younger face. 'Not just for me, but for you too. Please, Sam, try and understand. I can't help the way I feel about him.'

The only answer was a faint snore. Erin left her to sleep

it off, resolving, without too much hope, to try again in the morning on the way to school.

Nick was already down and waiting, a whisky to hand.

'Drink?' he asked.

Erin shook her head. 'No, thanks. Sam's asleep,' she added. 'Genuinely. I hope she doesn't wake up with a hangover.'

'It might teach her a lesson if she did,' Nick returned hardily. 'Playing the heavy father isn't exactly my scene.'

'You must be sick of the two of us,' she said, low-toned. 'We've been nothing but trouble to you.'

'You could say that.'

Erin gave him a swift glance, finding little reassurance in the ironic expression. 'It's not too late,' she steeled herself to say. 'If you want rid, you only have to—'

'Forget it.' His tone was brusque. 'What I start, I finish.' He drained the whisky glass and put it down. 'Let's go and eat.'

There was little conversation at table. Nick obviously wasn't in the mood for small talk, and Erin was too miserable to even attempt to dissemble.

If Bella recognised any untoward atmosphere, she kept her own counsel. Erin waited until she'd made a final departure before forcing herself to say what was on her mind.

'I really would understand if you decided to make other arrangements for the pair of us, Nick.'

'Such as what exactly?' he asked without particular inflection.

'Well, boarding-school for Sam, for a start.'

'Where she wouldn't stay, according to you.'

'She might. I suppose it would depend on the school.'

The grey eyes were unrevealing. 'And what other arrangement would you suggest for yourself?'

'You mentioned art college.' Erin's throat hurt so much

she could hardly get the words out. 'I realise it would cost a lot, but—'

'For God's sake, will you stop thinking in terms of cost!' Nick exploded. 'I don't give a damn about money!'

'You would, if you didn't have so much of it.' She went on doggedly, 'It wouldn't just be the college fees. I'd need somewhere to live too. It wouldn't have to be high-class, of course. I'd be more than happy to share a room.'

'You're not going anywhere!' Nick sounded as if he was fast reaching the end of his tether. 'Neither of you. I'll deal with whatever your sister comes up with as and when. As for you...'

He got to his feet, crossing the small space between them to yank her up into his arms, crushing her lips beneath his in a kiss that held little tenderness, eyes glittering with an anger she didn't fully understand.

'You're not going anywhere,' he repeated.

'I don't want to go anywhere,' she assured him thickly. 'I just thought—'

'Then don't think.' He was in control of himself again, the anger giving way to wryness. One hand came up to smooth back the tumbled hair from her face in much the same way she had done with Samantha's. 'We'll work it out.'

Erin ached to hear him say he loved her, but he obviously wasn't going to. He was marrying her because she'd played on his guilt. Oh, he still wanted her—last night proved that much—but how long before her unsophisticated responses became downright boring?

There were books one could learn from, she believed. If she could get hold of some such, she might at least stand a chance of maintaining his interest in that direction, and the rest could come in time. Meanwhile, she would just have to make the most of what she did have.

'Let's go to bed,' she said on a husky note, unable to

withstand the urges his touch and her thoughts combined were arousing in her.

Nick gave a faint smile. 'One of these days, I'll get to call the tune myself.'

Whatever else might be lacking, his lovemaking left absolutely nothing to be desired. Waking at daybreak to find herself still wrapped in his arms, Erin lay without moving a muscle, reluctant to relinquish the warm security of his embrace.

They were in her bed this time, not his. So far as she was concerned it didn't matter which room they shared, just so long as they were together. Waiting until they were married to see the whole night through was ridiculous on the face of it. She wanted to waken every morning like this, his arm heavy across her waist, his hand at her breast, his breath ruffling the hair at her nape. What difference was a piece of paper going to make?

She held her breath as he stirred, torn between conflicting desires.

'You awake?' he asked softly.

'No,' she said, and heard his low laugh.

'It's late. I should be going.'

The feel of his lips as he gently kissed the sensitive hollow was enough to reduce her to quivering jelly. She rolled onto her back, reaching up blindly to pull the lean face down to hers and kiss him with all the pent-up emotion of the last fifteen minutes.

'I won't let you go!' she whispered fiercely.

Supporting himself on an elbow, Nick looked down into passionate blue eyes with a smile that didn't quite reach his own. 'Much as I appreciate the enthusiasm, there's such a thing as moderation. Go back to sleep.'

There was no chance of that, she thought desolately, as he slid from the bed.

Samantha had still been out to the world when Erin had

made a last check on her. Finding her not only up but already dressed when she went to call her was quite a shock.

'No headache this morning?' she asked, prepared to be sympathetic.

'No,' her sister replied shortly. 'I didn't have *that* much to drink. And I don't need you checking up on me every five minutes either! It was bad enough last night, being dragged off in front of everybody like that! *He* had no right!'

Erin kept her tone reasonable. 'He's responsible for your welfare. Tim had no right to take you down there in the first place—especially without anyone knowing where you'd gone. Bella was going frantic when we got back.'

'It's none of *her* business what I do!'

'She was concerned that you might have got yourself lost.' Erin was having trouble hanging on to her temper. 'You should be grateful that people care enough to be worried—especially ones we've only known such a short time.' She paused, waiting for some easement in the mulish expression, giving vent to a sigh when it failed to materialise. 'You can't expect Nick to just let you do whatever you want, Sam.'

'Why not?' she retorted. 'You're the only one he cares about. I'm just in the way!'

'That's not true!' Erin took a step towards her, desisting in face of the fierce blue glare. 'You're his niece—his brother's only child. Of course he cares. Why else would he have brought you here when he could quite easily have sent you to some boarding-school and let others look after you?'

'He only did it because you wouldn't have come without me. I heard him persuading you that very first morning. He'd got the hots for you right away!'

'Will you stop using that stupid word!' Erin burst out.

'He needed me here to stop anyone getting any wrong ideas, that's all.'

'People were more likely to get them over you than me.' Sam was not to be pacified. 'I bet he got started on you that very first night when I left the two of you on your own!'

'Not true.' Erin was too upset to be angry any longer. 'It was me who made all the running. Me who told Harley we were going to be married. You said it yourself only yesterday, it would have taken someone a lot harder than Nick to make me tell everyone I was lying my head off.'

'He would have done it if he'd really wanted to.'

It was like batting her head against a brick wall, Erin acknowledged dispiritedly, viewing the set expression on her sister's face. Sam had got it into her mind that she was just a means to an end so far as Nick was concerned, and nothing was going to shake that conviction.

'We'd better get down for breakfast,' she said. 'You still have to go to school.'

'At least it gets me away from here!' was the only response.

Nick made no reference to the previous evening, and appeared not to notice his niece's uncustomary silence. The carriers worked to Caribbean time, he advised, when Erin asked when they were expected to come for the crates. It might even be tomorrow before they got here.

'I thought I might go straight into Bridgetown after I drop Sam off at school,' she said. 'Is there anything you need?'

'You could get me some shaving foam. I'm almost out.'

The idea of him wet-shaving was somehow far more alluring than if he had used an electric razor. Erin had a fleeting mental image of him standing before the bathroom mirror, a towel slung over one bare shoulder in readiness, each razor-stroke exposing smooth, firm skin. There was more than one kind of marital intimacy.

'Before I forget,' he added, 'Tessa rang while we were out yesterday. Her brother and his wife arrived yesterday. She wants us to go over to Bay Marris for dinner tonight and meet them.'

It was unlikely that the invitation included Sam. Unlikely that she'd want to come in any case. Erin felt none too keen on the idea of meeting more new people herself.

'What about Sam?' she asked when the latter went back upstairs to fetch a book she had forgotten. 'We can't leave her on her own for the whole evening.'

'We can't revolve our lives about her either,' Nick returned levelly. 'Bella and Josh will stay around till we get back.'

'To make sure she doesn't kick over the traces again?'

Her tone drew a cynical glance. 'You reckon I was too hard on her last night?'

'No.' Erin spread her hands in a wry gesture. 'I've never known her quite like this before.'

'She's never had Tim Wyman behind her before. If Val would put a curb on him we'd all benefit. Anyway, I'll see you when you get back.'

Samantha came back downstairs in silence, got into the car in silence, and kept her mouth tightly shut the whole journey. Reaching the school, she joined the incoming flow without so much as a glance, much less a goodbye.

It was all her fault, Erin acknowledged ruefully, heading for town. Even if it was true that Nick had been physically drawn to her, he would probably never have done anything about it if she hadn't thrown herself at his head.

She'd been lying to herself as well as to him in denying that she'd heard the car returning the night she went nude bathing in the pool. She'd wanted him to find her there. Sam was right in accusing her of using emotional blackmail. The price he had to pay, she'd told him; she couldn't have put it any plainer.

Still, if he wanted out he would have seized the opportunity she had offered him last night, she assured herself. And while it might take Sam a little while to get used to the idea, she would accept it in the end. She had to accept it. Everything was going to work out just fine!

CHAPTER TEN

WITH two cruise ships in dock, Bridgetown was thronged. Erin went back to the same boutique where she had bought the blue dress and purchased two more, along with some tailored shorts and a pair of white cotton trousers.

Enough for the present, she decided, already nervous over the amount she was spending. Wedding finery she refused to even contemplate until definite plans were made. She would prefer a church ceremony herself, but if Nick proved set on a quiet register office affair she was prepared to go along. The most important thing was the marriage itself, not where it took place.

Daydreaming about a rosy-hued future, she wandered through the stores. Most brides-to-be had to think about furnishing a home, but Malvern wanted for nothing—though she might at some point consider changing the colour scheme in the bedroom she and Nick would be sharing. This fabric she was looking at right now would make the most wonderful drapes. Outrageously expensive, of course, but cost was something she didn't have to worry about any more.

'I wouldn't make too many plans for spending Nick's money before you get that ring on your finger,' said a chilly voice at her back. 'He might come to his senses yet.'

Erin put a smile on her face as she turned to look at the last person she would have wanted to run into, feeling the corrosive impact of Dione's regard.

'He already did,' she said, and couldn't resist adding tauntingly, 'To the victor the spoils!'

146

The acrimony increased. 'You really think you've got it made, don't you?'

Erin made a rueful gesture, ashamed of the malicious remark. 'No, I don't. I shouldn't have said that. I wouldn't care if Nick didn't have a penny in the world!'

'Don't take me for an idiot,' came the scathing retort. 'I've been following you around this last twenty minutes, watching you finger your way through the stock. It's obvious you can hardly wait to get spending!'

Up until that moment Erin hadn't even realised that she'd wandered into Wyman's, of all places. She rallied with an effort.

'I'm surprised you've nothing better to do. Anyway, I have, if you'll excuse me.'

'You're living in a dream world if you imagine you can keep a man like Nick satisfied for long,' Dione thrust at her as she made to pass. 'He might have lost his head temporarily, but don't run away with the idea that a marriage licence is going to keep him chained to your bed!'

'I don't regard a marriage licence as any kind of entrapment,' Erin rejoined, hanging onto her dignity by a thread. 'As I said, if you'll excuse me.'

She walked away with head held high, aware of a trembling reaction in her lower limbs. The intimation had come across loud and clear as intended: when Nick got bored with her, then Dione would be there to offer solace. So it was going to be up to her to see that he didn't get bored.

The first bookshop she found had sections covering just about every subject under the sun barring the particular one she sought. She had to visit another two before discovering a solitary hardbacked manual on a bottom shelf.

The male assistant gave her a knowing look when she presented the book at the pay desk. Erin stared him down, not about to let him see any discomfiture. From her brief perusal of the contents, there was a whole lot she had to learn; she hadn't even realised there were more than a couple of positions in which to enjoy sex. Some of them looked more like wrestling than lovemaking, she had to admit, but if that was the way to keep a man stimulated then so be it. There were no lengths to which she wouldn't go to make this marriage work.

Nick had gone out when she got back. To where, Bella either genuinely didn't know or was deliberately acting dumb. Considering her general attitude since yesterday's announcement, Erin suspected the latter.

'I know you don't approve of what we're doing,' she said, deciding there was no point in beating about the bush, 'but I don't understand why.'

'Mr Nick needs a woman in his bed, not a child,' came the unequivocal return.

'I'm nineteen,' Erin protested. 'I'm sure a lot of Bajan girls are married at my age, or even younger!'

'You're not Bajan.'

Erin wanted to ask what the difference was, but doubted if a reply would be forthcoming. Like Sam, Bella would just have to come round to the idea. Nick's was the only opinion that mattered. He didn't *have* to marry her—ergo, he must really want to. What more did she need?

All the same, she had a struggle to stop herself from demanding to know where the devil he'd been when he finally put in an appearance halfway through the afternoon—especially when he made no attempt to tell her.

'I thought you wanted to be here in case they came for the crates on time,' she said by way of a hint.

'They did, for once,' he confirmed. 'Did you get everything you wanted?'

'For the moment, yes. I put the shaving foam in your bathroom. Three canisters.' Erin hesitated, unable in the end to stop herself from mentioning the name. 'I saw Dione in town.'

The grey eyes remained steady. 'Whereabouts in town?'

'The store. She was…rather nasty.'

'She probably thought you'd gone in there deliberately to provoke her.' Nick spoke calmly enough, but there was a certain tension about his mouth. 'Did you?'

'Of course not!' The denial was overheated; Erin made haste to tone her voice down. 'I didn't even realise I was in Wyman's until she spoke to me. I was looking at fabrics.'

'You reckon the house needs doing over?'

The irony stung, but she stood her ground. 'Not all of it, obviously, but I wouldn't mind getting rid of all those dark colours in your bedroom—assuming that's the one we'll be using?'

'Replacing it with what, exactly?'

It was time, Erin decided, to introduce a little humour into this conversation before it got out of hand. 'I rather fancy pink and gold myself,' she said blandly. 'With some animal prints thrown in for interest, perhaps.'

'Over my dead body!' Nick was smiling again, recognising the ploy for what it was.

Sitting there on the veranda, face bronzed by the sun, body leanly muscled beneath the tautly stretched white shirt, he made her ache. Fired by a need she couldn't have controlled if she'd wanted to, she got up and went to him, sliding down onto his knees to put her lips to his— breathing in the heady masculine scent of him.

He slid his fingers into the thickness of her hair to draw her closer, mouth taking over, pressuring hers apart, tasting the sweetness of soft inner flesh, his free hand seeking the tender curve of her breast. There was a growing heat radiating from the very pit of her stomach, a dampness between her thighs. She wanted his touch there too—the feel of him inside her.

Recalling something she had read in the book she had

bought, she abandoned his lips in order to run the tip of her tongue very, very lightly and slowly around the outer rim of his ear, feeling his immediate response. 'Let's go to bed,' she murmured. 'I want you, Nick!'

'Wrong time, I'm afraid,' he said after a moment. 'I'm expecting a phone call.' He kissed her again, more lightly this time, and put her back on her feet, registering her expression with a dry smile. 'If it's worth having, it's worth waiting for.'

'In other words, *you'll* decide where and when?' she flung at him, lacerated by the rejection. 'That's sheer chauvinism!'

'Prudence,' he corrected. 'I need to conserve my energies.'

Erin caught herself before she could let fly with a pithy rejoinder. It was good, according to the book, for the woman to take the initiative, but obviously not too often. Male pride was such a fragile affair!

'You know what they say about the first flush of enthusiasm soon wearing off,' she said, opting to make a joke of it. 'You'll have something to complain about when I start having headaches!'

'I'll keep a good stock of aspirin.'

There was a pause while he studied her as she leaned against the veranda rail. When he spoke again it was on a cogitative note. 'I believe you have to stop taking the Pill for a week every month in order to have your period. How many more days before you're due to take the break?'

Erin hesitated, unable to stop a guilty flush from staining her cheeks. 'I'd have to check,' she mumbled.

The grey eyes narrowed a fraction. 'What are you hiding?'

'Nothing,' she denied. 'Like I said, I'd have to—' She broke off, lifting her shoulders resignedly. 'All right, I've gone a few days over. There's no harm in it.'

'Scared of nothing happening when you do stop?' he asked softly.

'Of finding I'm pregnant, you mean?' She shook her head emphatically. 'It's a remote chance anyway, but it wouldn't worry me.'

'Then why—' It was Nick's turn to break off, his lips twisting. 'It didn't fit in with your plans for the weekend, right?'

'It wasn't like you're making it sound,' Erin protested. 'I wanted you to make love to me again, yes, but I didn't plan what happened Saturday night. It just...did. I'm not even capable of concocting a plot like that!'

'Not until you got together with Tessa Marshall, at any rate.'

'Don't blame Tessa,' she pleaded.

'I don't,' he said. 'I blame myself.' He paused, eyeing her dispassionately. 'You'd better take the break now. This time next week we'll be married. I already made the arrangements. Sorry if you were counting on a lavish affair. I'd prefer to keep it low-key.'

Erin dropped to her knees beside his chair, laying her cheek against his bare arm. 'I don't care how low-key it is! I just want us to be together.'

The burr of the telephone cut off any reply he had been about to make. She lifted her head as he reached for the extension at his other elbow, watching his face for some indication of who the call might be coming from.

'Isn't it time you were going to pick Sam up?' he asked, covering the mouthpiece for a moment.

It was indeed, she realised, looking at his watch. She got reluctantly to her feet. 'See you when we get back,' she said in the ridiculous way one did.

'I'll be here,' he returned easily.

'Tomorrow will be fine,' he told the listener on the other end of the line as she went indoors. 'Let's make it eleven.'

A business meeting, Erin told herself firmly, and wished she could wholly believe it.

The flood of emerging students had already dried to a trickle when she reached the college. Sam wasn't waiting at the gates. Nor was anyone Erin asked able to tell her where her sister might be.

About to go in to make further enquiries, she was torn between relief and exasperation on seeing the girl come strolling out, as if time was of no importance, Tim Wyman at her side.

'I've been waiting nearly ten minutes!' she exclaimed. 'What on earth have you been doing?'

'Not a lot, compared with you,' came the smart retort, bringing a grin to Tim's face. 'Anyway, you don't need to come and pick me up any more. I'll be getting a lift.'

Erin forced a milder note. 'Thanks Tim, but it isn't necessary. Come on, Sam.'

'Better do as big sister tells you,' Tim advised derisively as the younger girl hesitated. 'We don't want Uncle Nick on the warpath again. See you tomorrow.'

Sam got into the Mercedes as he moved away, pretty face set. 'You're just as bad as *he* is!' she fumed. 'Why can't you both just leave me alone?'

'You know why.' Erin had had enough of diplomacy. 'You can't be trusted to act responsibly.'

'And you can, of course! I bet it's true what people are saying!'

The best thing would be to ignore the comment, Erin knew, but she couldn't. 'What *are* they saying?'

'That he's got to marry you because you're pregnant!'

No such thing as a hundred per cent guarantee, Nick had said, but the chances were infinitesimal, Erin was sure.

'Well, they're wrong,' she rejoined flatly, starting the engine. 'I'm not.'

Sam looked unconvinced. 'Why else would he choose you instead of Dione? Tim says they were a regular item.'

'That doesn't mean he wanted to marry her.'

'It means he was doing it with her before he did it with you!'

The crudity of it set Erin's teeth on edge. Those were Tim's words, not her sister's. 'I wouldn't let Nick hear you coming out with things like that,' she said, trying not to let her thoughts dwell on the implications. 'He'd wash your mouth out with soap!'

'I'd bite his fingers off if he tried!' There was a pause, a sly glance. 'You have, though, haven't you?'

Erin kept her eyes fixed firmly on the car ahead of them on the narrow road. 'Have what?'

'Done it.' She used the phrase with deliberation. 'What's it like?'

'Stop it, Sam—please!' Erin was past being angry. 'Try and understand. I love him!'

The plea struck deaf ears. 'If you marry him I'll never speak to you again!' declared the younger girl fiercely. 'I mean it, Rin!'

Erin let it lie. For the time being at least. Much as she loved Sam, she couldn't contemplate doing as she demanded—if Nick would agree to it to start with. The arrangements were made, the date set: a week hence they would be man and wife. Between then and now she had to somehow talk her sister into accepting things the way they were.

She'd forgotten about the Marshalls' invitation, and was on the verge of making some excuse not to go until she realised that by doing so she would be giving Sam the wrong impression. They left her watching television in sullen silence, with Bella to keep an eye on her from time to time.

'I'm getting close to losing patience with that young

lady,' Nick admitted in the car. 'A boarding-school might be the best answer after all.'

'She'll be okay,' Erin assured him hastily. 'I think she's just a bit jealous, that's all.'

The dark brows drew together. 'Of what?'

'Not what. Who.' Erin crossed her fingers in her lap. 'She has a crush on you herself.'

Nick tilted a sardonic lip. 'Sure she has!'

'It's true.' Having said it, Erin felt bound to follow through. 'It's part of growing up.'

'You being past that stage yourself, of course.'

She gave the lean, hard profile a swift glance. 'Way past. I'm truly, madly in love with you!'

'So you keep telling me.'

More than he ever told her, came the thought, swiftly thrust aside. 'I'm going to keep right on doing it too,' she said, 'so you'd better get used to it.' She put a hand on his thigh, feeling the muscle tense as she slid it slowly and tantalisingly upward. 'It's going to be a long week!'

'Cut it out,' he ordered, sounding anything but lover-like. 'You'll have us off the road!'

She withdrew the hand immediately, appreciative of the reason if not the tone. 'Sorry, I wasn't thinking.'

He made no reply, expression austere. Erin made a silent vow to be a little more circumspect in her behaviour. It was just so darn difficult to resist the urge to touch him. Her fingers itched even now to smooth their way along his freshly shaven jawline. His very maturity excited her. Who would want a boy when they had a real man?

Shaded by tropical evergreens, the old plantation house that was Bay Marris welcomed them with open doors and a revitalised decor.

Erin was glad she had worn the deceptively simple little black dress the saleswoman had persuaded her was worth every penny of its cost on seeing the equally simple but obviously expensive outfits Tessa and her sister-in-law were wearing. With her hair taken up again, and poised on high heels, she felt able to hold her own with anyone.

Tessa's brother, Oliver, proved to be around Nick's age, Elizabeth a couple of years or so younger. They had a son of ten and a daughter of eight, both of them at present being looked after by their maternal grandparents back in Los Angeles.

Ten years from now, she and Nick could be in a similar position, Erin reflected, caught up in a familiar daydream. He would still only be in his mid-forties, while she would be a mature twenty-nine. Tessa was right: the gap did narrow.

It was an enjoyable evening all round. Oliver kept them entertained with a fund of amusing stories about the advertising business. Erin was impressed to learn that he was the producer of a number of major TV advertisements.

'We've sometimes had American ads in England,' she said, talking with him later. 'There was one particularly funny one with a couple of men trying to repair a car and everything going wrong.'

Oliver shook his head. 'Not one of mine. What was the product, anyway?'

'To be honest,' she confessed, 'I was always too busy laughing to take much notice.'

'The client was wasting his money, then.'

'I suppose so. I never thought of it like that before.'

'Neither do many of the writers. Too intent on the visual impact.' He paused, a smile on his face as he studied her. 'Nick's a lucky man.'

Nick was talking with Bryn down the other end of the veranda. They could almost be father and son, Erin thought fleetingly.

'I'm the lucky one,' she said.

Oliver laughed. 'I can remember Tessa saying the same thing about Bryn.'

'How did you react when you found out she was going to marry him?' asked Erin with some diffidence. 'You'd only be about seven or eight at the time, I imagine?'

'Eight,' he confirmed. 'I wasn't too impressed at first.'

'But you obviously came round to it?'

'I had a whole new life of my own to think about. We used to live just down the hill. Bryn inherited Bay Marris from his grandfather and decided to turn it into a country club as he wasn't going to be around a great deal owing to his job. He bought our house and land to form part of the golf course when Mom married Roland and we moved down to his place. A house with its own private beach and boat was pure paradise to an eight-year-old.' His gaze was shrewd. 'Your sister giving you trouble, is she?'

'Some,' Erin admitted.

'She'll accept it once you and Nick are married—even more so when you make her an aunt. You do plan on having children?'

'Definitely. Two at least.'

'Well, I wouldn't leave it too long to get started. Nick might not find the patter of little feet all that appealing in his forties.'

There was still a chance, no matter how remote, that they'd already started, Erin reflected. Even after leaving off the Pill, it was going to be a couple of days before she knew for sure.

Tessa joined them, addressing her brother with sisterly candour. 'Go and keep your wife company while we talk women's talk.'

'I can't tell you how happy I am that it all worked out for you,' she continued, sliding into the chair he'd obligingly vacated. 'I loved the way you put Dione down Saturday night!'

Erin lifted her shoulders in a rueful little gesture. 'I shouldn't have said it.'

'Of course you should. She asked for it. Anyway, you weren't all that premature.'

'It's going to be a very quiet affair,' Erin felt bound to emphasise. 'Apart from you and Bryn, I'm not even sure who'll be coming.' She shrank from admitting that so far she didn't even know the venue. 'It will have to be word of mouth, in any case. There isn't going to be time to get invitations printed.'

'Well, the Wymans won't be there for certain—though my mother will certainly be rooting for you. Roland too, if I know him at all. Val was always the self-important one. As you haven't any family apart from your sister, and you don't really know anyone else on the island, then I suppose it has to be up to Nick to decide who else he wants to invite.'

Erin supposed so too. It wasn't important anyway. The only thing she cared about was the wedding itself.

'It's a pity Oliver and Elizabeth are only here until Sunday,' she said in the car going home. 'It would have been nice to have someone our own age group.'

'My age group, at any rate,' Nick rejoined. 'Apart from Sam, I'm afraid that's as close as it's going to get to yours. One of the penalties of marrying an older man.'

'Not so far as I'm concerned,' Erin assured him. 'I've told you before, people my age are boring. All most of them are interested in is having a good time.'

'You've never had the opportunity to do the things most teenagers do,' Nick pointed out. 'How do you know you'd have found it all so boring?'

'I just do, that's all. And I did have the opportunity. I wasn't a prisoner.'

'You lacked the funds to be anything else but.'

There was some truth in that, Erin had to admit. And,

yes, there had been times when she would have liked to get dressed up and go out somewhere. Only never to discos and pubs; that scene hadn't interested her one iota.

'You'll just have to take my word for it that I don't see myself as having missed out on anything,' she declared. 'And I'm not doing it now either. I'm as happy as Larry! I wonder who Larry was?' she tagged on with genuine curiosity.

'Probably a galloping depressive,' he said.

'It's a good job I know you're not the cynic you make yourself out to be,' she mocked back, and saw his mouth take on a different slant.

'You reckon you know me so well?'

'Well enough,' she said firmly. 'I wouldn't want to know you through and through—any more than I'd want you to know everything there was to know about me. There'd be no surprises left.'

He gave her a quizzical glance. 'Something else you once read somewhere?'

'I do have *some* original thoughts,' she retorted in mock indignation. 'You're not marrying some dumb blonde!'

'That I can vouch for,' he agreed drily.

Erin was silent for a moment. When she spoke again it was on a subdued note. 'You said that very first night that you'd never met a woman you could contemplate living with full time. Do you still find it difficult?'

'The idea's growing on me. Given time, I may even get to like it.'

Erin had to laugh, although it was far from the answer she would have liked. If she hadn't come on the scene, Nick might well have opted to stay a bachelor for life. He wouldn't have been deprived of feminine company, for certain.

It was gone midnight when they reached the house. Erin

demurred when Nick attempted to kiss her goodnight at her
bedroom door.

'It's going to be two or three days before I start,' she
said softly. 'You already turned me down once today. If
you do it again, I'll start to wonder if you really want me
at all!'

'You're too forward for your own good,' he remonstrated
lightly. 'I've half a mind to turn you down just to emphasise who wears the trousers round here.' Looking at the
lovely young face upturned to his, he gave a wry smile.
'Unfortunately, the flesh is weaker than the spirit. We'd
better go to my room.'

'I'm already as protected as I need to be,' Erin protested,
guessing the reason. 'I want you as Nature intended, not
covered in cling film!'

Nick hastily stifled the involuntary laugh, eyes dancing.
'You,' he said, 'are an out-and-out hussy! Get in there!'

'Age before beauty,' she returned blandly, inviting him
ahead of her.

It was her turn to muffle laughter as he swept her up and
bore her into the room, burying her face in his jacket lapel.
So thrillingly assertive, this man of hers. So thrillingly *everything*! A lifetime spent with him wasn't going to be
nearly long enough.

Tossing her down on the bed, he stood up to slough both
jacket and shirt, shoulders silvered against the moonlit window at his back. 'I'll do the undressing,' he said posses-
sively when she sat up to reach for the fastening at her
nape.

'You're the one wearing the trousers,' she responded de-
murely, lying down again to watch with mounting anticipation as he stripped them off along with everything else.

He came down on the bed-edge, supporting his weight
on hands placed either side of her as he bent to put his lips

to hers with a tantalising, infinitely light brushing motion that sent her pulse-rate soaring.

'A regular hussy,' he repeated softly. 'I can see I'm going to have real trouble with you in time to come.'

'I'll look forward to being dealt with,' she murmured, hungry for more. 'Any way you like!'

Something flared deep down in the grey eyes. This time his lips were less gentle, demanding not asking a response. Erin gave it without restraint, fingers curling into the crisp thickness of his hair, every sense tuned to the feel of him, the scent of him, the roughened sound of his breathing.

She had already kicked off her sandals. Lifting one bare foot, she slid her toes slowly and sensuously down the side of his calf and back again, bringing her body into more intimate contact where it mattered most—pressing herself against him with an urgency impossible to resist.

The black dress gave at the seam as he lifted it over her head without bothering to unzip it. As before, she was wearing nothing but a pair of skimpy lace panties beneath. Nick took those off too, kissing his way down the length of her body to the shadowed joining of her thighs. It was only the sudden memory of Sam in the very next room that kept her from giving way to the sounds jerked from her throat at the sensations conjured by the marauding mouth. It was almost too much to bear. If he didn't stop, she would explode!

When he did stop, that was almost too much to bear either. She reached for him, allowing her instincts to guide her as she mastered the movement, seeing the lean features contort, hearing his breathing roughen, stimulated even further by the pleasure she was affording him. There was so much she still didn't know, but she was learning. All the time she was learning! She was going to make sure he never had need to seek other women for satisfaction. Never, never, never!

She was more than halfway to the peak already when he moved over her, supporting himself on his elbows to join his body to hers. Erin stifled her cries against the dark curls of hair on his chest as the long, slow strokes gathered momentum, unable to fully let go for fear of the girl next door overhearing the sounds. They should have done as Nick wanted in the first place, and gone to his room!

It was her last coherent thought for some time. Emerging slowly from total enervation, she found herself still wrapped tight in Nick's arms, although lying on her side now, facing him.

His eyes were open, looking directly into hers, the smile on his lips reflecting her own sentiments.

'Better and better!' he said.

'You mean it wasn't all that good the other times?' she asked, only half joking.

He gave a low laugh. 'I mean you're a source of constant revelation. You almost had me over the top back there!'

'Your own fault for being too good a tutor.'

'I don't have to be. Your instincts are sound enough.' He kissed the end of her small straight nose, making no attempt to let her go. 'It seems I have a lot to thank David for.'

'Me too,' she whispered. 'I didn't want him to die, of course, but I might never have known you if he hadn't.' She put her fingers to his lips. 'Please don't start on about my meeting someone else. It could never have been like this!'

'You'll never know,' he said. 'Unless you ditch me at some later date, of course.'

'Not in a million years! Well, the next sixty or so, at any rate!'

'In sixty years I'll be ninety-four, if I'm here at all,' Nick observed drily.

'You'll still be the same man.' She stirred uncomfortably. 'I need to go to the bathroom.'

He released her with obvious reluctance. 'Hurry back. The night's still young.'

Sleep was the last thing on her mind too, she could have told him, but he would know soon enough. The fact that he wanted her again was a boost in itself. The book wasn't needed. As he had said, her instincts were sound enough. She would give free rein to them from now on, she thought exultantly.

CHAPTER ELEVEN

NICK was sitting up in bed with the bedside lamp on and the book she had left lying carelessly on the cabinet top open in his hands when she came out from the bathroom. The expression on his face as he looked across at her was more than a little disquieting.

'Where did *this* come from?' he clipped.

'I bought it.' Unable to understand his attitude, Erin found herself stumbling a little for words. 'I wanted to know how to keep you...satisfied.'

'And you think sexual acrobatics are going to do it?'

'Well, no, not on their own.' She became suddenly and self-consciously aware that she was standing there without a stitch on, with nothing in the least lover-like about the way he was looking at her. 'I thought it might help if I knew a little more about what men like, that's all.'

'Well, you obviously studied the right page for tonight's performance.'

The sarcasm hurt. Even more so because it wasn't true. 'That was nothing to do with what I'd read,' she said huskily. 'I'd already realised there are things no book can teach.' She made a gesture of appeal. 'I love you, Nick! I just want to make you happy.'

There was no relaxing of the ironically tilted lips, no softening of tone. 'You could get what I give you from any man.'

'No!' Oblivious now both of her nudity and the possibility of listening ears next door, Erin went to him, snatching the book from his hands and hurling it across the room.

'You're the only man I want! You're the only man I'll *ever* want!'

The grey eyes were veiled. 'I'm the only man you've known in any intimate sense. Maybe we should hang fire until you've some basis for comparison.'

'What do you plan on doing?' she countered in outrage. 'Hiring someone to provide it for me?'

The veil lifted, revealing a steely glint. 'Your sister's next door. Do you want to waken her?'

Erin bit her lip. It was very likely already too late. The cotton wrap she had bought on a last-minute impulse that morning was draped over the bottom of the bed. She reached for it, dragging it about her with numbed fingers, the painted image looming too large in her mind's eye to withstand the need to cover herself. Nick already had a basis for comparison.

'All this over a stupid book!' she said, trying and failing to keep her voice steady. 'I hadn't even got round to more than just leafing through it.'

'It isn't just the book.' Nick sounded suddenly weary. 'It's the whole affair. I need my head examining for ever letting things get this far!'

Eyes dark, mouth vulnerable, she stood there like a statue as he threw back the sheet and slid from the bed. Her impulse was to throw herself at him and refuse to accept what he appeared to be telling her, but pride held her back.

'I suppose it's lucky you came to your senses in time,' she got out through a throat that felt as if it were coated with sandpaper.

He finished pulling on his trousers before answering, his back to her. 'In time for what?'

'To cancel the wedding arrangements.'

'There's no question of that. I told you before, what I start, I finish.'

Erin gazed at the broad bare back, hardly knowing what to feel. 'Supposing *I* decide to cancel it!'

'You won't.'

The surging anger was a refuge from the hurt inflicted by that flat statement. Scooping up the small china clock from the bedside table, she flung it at him, missing his head by inches to hit the wall beyond with a crash that jerked the back of her hand up to her mouth in realisation of what she might have achieved.

'Nick, I'm sorry!' she said shakily as he turned. 'I could have killed you!'

'Not with an aim like that.' If he was angry, he was concealing it well. He studied her flushed young face with a certain wryness in the line of his mouth. '*Do* you want to cancel?'

'You know I don't. You just told me so.' Erin made an effort to inject certainty into her voice. 'I really do love you, Nick.'

The smile was faint. 'You have a very forceful way of showing it.'

'I never did anything like that before in my life,' she said ruefully. 'I never will again either.'

'Never's a long time—although I wouldn't count on quite the same tolerance in future. Just make sure to gather up the bits before Bella sees them,' he added. 'She'll notice the thing's missing, so you'll have to say you dropped it. It's well insured.'

Blue eyes widened in dismay. 'Was it *very* valuable?'

'Fairly.' Nick lifted a quizzical eyebrow. 'Would it have made a difference?'

'I don't suppose so,' she conceded. 'I was too wound up to think about it.' She gave an involuntary little laugh. 'No pun intended!'

Her smile faded as Nick picked up his shirt. 'You're still going?'

'Considering the likelihood that Sam's wide awake and all ears by now, I think it might be the best policy,' he said. 'Anyway, it's time we both got some sleep.'

They could sleep together, Erin wanted to point out, but knew she would be wasting her breath. He was right too: Sam couldn't possibly have slept through the noise the clock had made crashing against the party wall. Considering the circumstances, there was every chance that they wouldn't be making love again at all until after the wedding. A whole week to wait. She didn't think she could live that long!

It took every ounce of self-control she had to hold back when Nick kissed her goodnight.

'Sweet dreams,' he said softly, and went.

Erin took off the wrap and got back into bed, burying her face in the pillow he had used. She wasn't going to sleep a wink without the warmth and comfort of his arms about her. Not a solitary wink!

The confirmation a couple of days later that she wasn't pregnant gave rise to mixed feelings. On the one hand regret, because it would have been wonderful to be having Nick's baby, on the other relief, because he might not have wanted to make love to her at all when she got fat. He certainly showed no regrets when she told him the news.

Despite what Oliver had said, there was plenty of time anyway, Erin assured herself. They could well afford to wait another year or two.

In the meantime, relations with her sister were little improved. Samantha had made no mention of being woken up the night of the clock-throwing incident, but her attitude the next morning had made it obvious, to Erin at least, that she had not only heard the noise but put her own interpretation on it.

Nick's tolerance was beginning to wear very thin. If she

didn't stop acting the brat, he was going to start treating her like one, he threatened.

'You wouldn't dare!' she retorted, with a contempt that made Erin wince. 'It's against the law for you to lay a finger on me!'

Grey eyes sparked. 'It might be in England. Don't count on it being the same here. It doesn't matter what you think of me. Erin's the one you're hurting.'

He might have been talking to a brick wall for all the difference it was making, thought Erin unhappily, viewing the stubborn set of her sister's mouth. Sam was heading for a fall if she pushed him much further.

It was all on her head, of course. She'd had no one's interests but her own at heart when she'd set out to get her man. Nick himself had been trapped into making a commitment he wasn't wholly ready for.

She could put everything to rights by backing out on the marriage, but the strength of mind that it would take to do that was beyond her. Sooner or later Sam had to realise that no matter how much she played up she wasn't going to change anything. Hopefully it would be the former not the latter.

The lovely old church in St Andrew where the wedding was to take place was set on a hilltop with wonderful views of the Atlantic coastline. Nick had taken her to meet the pastor, and then down to view the very up-market Sandy Lane Hotel where he had arranged a reception for the dozen or so people invited, most of whom Erin had still to meet. The friend he'd asked to be his best man was due to fly in from New York on Sunday.

With Tessa's help, Erin extended her wardrobe to take her through a honeymoon in some definitely warm but otherwise unknown location. The dress she chose to be married in was a simple affair in white broderie anglaise. No veil or hat, she decided, just a small spray of flowers to match the one she would be carrying.

'You're going to look positively angelic!' Tessa stated after whisking her off to lunch at the Hilton. 'You should leave your hair down on the day, spread over your shoulders like a golden cape!'

'I'll probably look more like Alice in Wonderland if I do,' Erin rejoined laughingly. 'I think Nick would rather I added a year or two.' She sobered a little. 'I still feel guilty about the way I conned him into this.'

'I very much doubt if he would have gone along with it if he hadn't wanted to,' said Tessa reassuringly. 'All right, it might not have happened as soon, but it would have happened eventually, I'm certain. It's obvious to everybody that he's crazy about you!'

'Not to me. At least, not in the way you mean.' Erin hesitated before saying it. 'He's never once told me he loves me.'

'Well, men don't find it all that easy a word to use. Not really macho, and all that. Wait till you're on honeymoon. It's surprising how much more emotional they become once they get to the bridal suite. Something to do with having finally plighted their troth, maybe.'

Erin had to smile. 'I'll take your word for it.'

There was a pause while they both sampled the wine. When Tessa spoke again it was on a different tack.

'Oliver told me you were having trouble with your sister. Has she come round to it yet?'

Considering that Sam was still adamant about not coming to the wedding, there was no point in putting up a pretence, Erin acknowledged. 'No,' she admitted. 'She thinks the whole thing is utterly revolting.'

'How is Nick coping with it?'

'Well enough, up to now, but I'm afraid he's going to finish up really losing his temper.'

'Might be the best thing for her.'

Erin shook her head emphatically. 'She'd hate him for ever!'

'Then you'll just have to wait for her to grow up enough to recognise that she isn't the only axis your world turns on.'

Easily said, not so easily done, Erin reflected. No one could force Sam to attend the wedding, as Nick had already said. All she could hope was that, come the day, she would at least relent that far. It certainly wouldn't be the same without her.

It was no help to get to the college later that afternoon and learn that Sam had defied her and gone off in Tim's car. If Nick found out about this he was really going to blow his top! she thought worriedly.

With no idea at all of where else they might have gone, she headed for home in the hope of finding them somewhere along the way, breathing a sigh of relief when she came on the bright red open-top parked some quarter of a mile from the gates.

Neither of the occupants looked in the least bit discomfited when Erin drew up alongside. She suspected they'd been kissing, although as college rules forbade the wearing of lipstick there was no actual proof of it.

'You won't be so pleased with yourselves if Nick gets to know what you're up to!' she said searingly. 'You'd better get in here, Sam. And *you'd* better take warning, Tim!'

His grin mocked her anger. 'I'm shaking in my shoes! See you tomorrow, honey,' he added as Sam slid from the car.

She gave him a smile and a wave before getting into the Mercedes, the former disappearing as Erin put the car into jerky motion.

'I told you you didn't need to come for me any more.'

'And I told you no go,' Erin retorted. 'Tim Wyman is far too old for you!'

'Listen who's talking!' came the scathing response.

'It's different for me.'

'You're not kidding! Nick's nearly old enough to be *your* father!'

It was what she had told herself once, Erin acknowledged, but only in defence from the emotions he had aroused in her. 'I mean it's different because I'm of an age to be sure of how I feel,' she said. 'There's nothing wrong with having a boyfriend at fourteen, but not someone like Tim Wyman. He's just out to score points.'

'You don't know him! You don't know anything!' The younger girl was beside herself with anger. 'Why don't you go and ask Tim what your precious Nick gets up to when he goes out on his own?'

They had nearly reached the gates. Erin drew to a stop at the roadside to sit gazing blindly through the windscreen for a slow, ticking moment.

'What are you talking about?' she got out.

'He's been meeting Dione. Tim saw them together yesterday afternoon, driving down to Frame Cove. It's nice and private down there, especially in the week.'

Some time soon, Erin knew, the pain had to start, but right now all she felt was numb. Nick hadn't been home when she'd got back with Sam yesterday afternoon, and he'd offered no explanation when he did put in an appearance around six-thirty.

'Rin?' The belligerence had gone from her sister's voice, replaced by something approaching abashment. 'Say something.'

'What would you like me to say?' Erin asked tonelessly.

'I don't know. Call me a liar. Anything!'

A spark momentarily lit the dullness of the other blue eyes. 'Are you lying?'

Sam hesitated before slowly shaking her head. 'It could have been perfectly innocent, though.'

And pigs might fly! thought Erin, feeling the numbness vanish as her imagination began filling in the picture. She had never been to this Frame Cove herself, though Sam obviously had—the question of how and when still to be resolved. Unlikely to be visited by others during the week, which made it the ideal place for a tryst. She could see the two of them lying together under the shade of a palm tree, the sunlight filtering through the gently waving fronds onto bare bronzed skin. Dione would have no need of books to tell her what a man might like; she would know it all!

'We'd better get back,' she said, unable to bear any further envisaging. 'Bella will have had tea ready for ages.'

They were through the gates and heading up the drive before Sam spoke. She sounded subdued. 'What are you going to do?'

'I don't know,' Erin responded hollowly. 'Face him with it, I suppose. Give him a chance to explain.' Sensing the reaction from the girl at her side, she gave a wry little shrug. 'You're right. What's the point?'

'You wouldn't still marry him, would you?' asked Sam as they drew up at the house. 'I mean, you *can't* still think you love somebody who'd do that to you!'

Lack of trust in itself was no basis for marriage, Erin reflected. Nick had been prepared to go through with it because she had brought unfair pressure to bear on him, but there was no way she was ever going to be able to give him what a woman like Dione could give him. It was better for them both that they called time on the whole relationship.

'No, I shan't be marrying him,' she confirmed in the same expressionless tones. 'I'll tell him I changed my mind. But in my own time,' she added. 'You're not to say anything about this to anyone!'

'Of course not.' Sam sounded subdued again, as if only just beginning to realise what she'd set in motion. 'What about all the arrangements?'

'They'll have to be unarranged.' Erin thought of the bags piled up in the car boot, and steeled herself. 'It's only Thursday. There's time enough.'

Bella's appearance in the house doorway put paid to any reply Sam might have been going to make.

'I got tea set ready!' she scolded. 'What are the both of you doin'?'

'We're just coming,' Erin answered, opening the car door. 'Sorry, Bella.'

The housekeeper's annoyance faded as she surveyed the pale young face and lacklustre eyes. 'You got a bad feelin' in your stomach, child?' she asked on a sympathetic note.

'Must be something I've eaten,' Erin answered, seizing on the excuse as a way of giving her time to think. 'I'm going to go and lie down for a bit.'

'You do that. I'll tell Mr Nick where you're at.'

'It's best if I just try and sleep it off,' Erin said hastily, nowhere near ready to face Nick as yet.

'I'll come up and sit with you,' offered Sam.

Erin shook her head. 'I need to be on my own.'

It was obvious from her expression that Sam was reluctant to face Nick herself. Erin almost relented, but self-interest won the day for once. She *had* to be on her own.

The bedroom she had shared more than once with Nick proved no retreat. She went out onto the balcony, to sit gazing down at the pool where it had all begun, heart and mind heavy as lead.

Bella must have served tea on the veranda, she realised, hearing the sound of her sister's voice, although not the words themselves. Nick replied in even quieter tones, eliciting a sudden rise in Sam's decibel level.

'It's *you* she's sick of! She doesn't want to marry you any more! She told me so!'

Erin sat frozen, waiting for Nick's reply, but none came. She heard the sudden scrape of chair legs on wooden boards, the sound of footsteps heading indoors, then silence. He would be coming up here, she thought in panic, and she wasn't ready for him! Thanks to her loud-mouthed little sister, she hadn't even had time to consider what she was going to say to him.

The door had a lock, of course. For a fleeting moment she contemplated rushing across and turning the key. But what was the use? No matter how long she put it off, it had to be faced in the end. Best to get it over with now.

She was sitting in one of the easy chairs when Nick came in without bothering to knock. He closed the door quietly and stood looking across at her, face impassive.

'Feeling better?' he asked.

Erin moved her head in slow negation, fighting for the control to see this through without giving way to the urge to throw the whole thing in his face. 'Not so you'd notice.'

There was a lengthy pause. Nick made no attempt to advance further into the room, nor did he reveal what he might be thinking.

'I understand you might have something to tell me.'

'Yes.' She swallowed the hard lump forming in her throat, forcing herself to carry on. 'I've…changed my mind about marrying you.'

'Just like that?'

'No, not just like that.' She cast around for some plausible reason. 'I suppose not being pregnant after all had something to do with it.'

'You never really believed you were to start with,' he returned in the same unemotional tones, 'so why would it make a difference to how you feel?'

'I don't know why, it just did,' Erin said doggedly. 'I

realised today that I'd been living in a dream world the last few weeks—a romantic dream world. I thought because I liked having you make love to me that I had to be in love with you.'

'But now you know you're not?'

'Now I know I'm not.' It was all she could do to force the words out, because they weren't true. Love didn't die because the recipient of it turned out to be unworthy. That was something else she had learned. 'I'm...sorry,' she tagged on lamely. 'I realise how much trouble I've put you to—to say nothing of the expense. I—'

She broke off, seeing the sudden glitter in the grey eyes, the hardened line of his jaw.

'Better you came to your senses now than after the ceremony. I'll take care of everything. You just concentrate on what you want to do from here on in.'

Do? She hadn't got that far. One thing she couldn't do was stay on here, though. Nick himself would probably be glad to see the back of her.

'I want to go home,' she said. 'Back to England. Only not at your expense—or at least, no more expense. I charged everything today, like you said, so I still have the majority of the money you put to my account. That will buy me my return ticket, and tide me over for a few days while I get things sorted out. Social Services will find me somewhere to live.'

'Do you really think I'm going to agree to that?' Nick demanded harshly.

'You don't really have a choice,' she said. 'I was never your responsibility.'

'Sam is,' he reminded her. 'You're willing to leave her?'

Erin braced herself against the anguish. 'I can hardly take her with me, can I?'

'No,' he agreed hardily. 'She'll just have to manage without you.' He straightened away from the door. 'It might

be best if we stay out of each other's way for the present.
I'll get Bella to bring you up a tray later. She'll be glad to
hear you're on the road to recovery.'

She would no doubt be even more so to hear that the
wedding was off, thought Erin painfully, willing herself to
defy the urge to call him back as the door closed in his
wake. Even if she had faced him with what she knew it
would have made no difference to the outcome. Once he
got over the anger he must be feeling inside over all the
trouble she had caused him, he could only be relieved to
have his life back in order again. Dione would see to it that
he didn't lack satisfaction—or, if not her, there were plenty
of other women around.

One thing he definitely wouldn't be doing from now on
was taking an interest in teenage girls. They were far too
prone to cause problems.

Arriving with the promised dinner tray some couple of
hours later, Bella fussed over her like a mother hen.

'You eat up now!' she admonished as Erin listlessly
picked over the chicken casserole. 'That'll make you feel
better.'

'I'm sure it will,' Erin answered. 'I'm just not very hungry, that's all.'

'Just try, then,' encouraged the woman. 'You've still
some growin' to do, chil'.'

Not any more, Erin reflected, alone again. She had seen
the very last of her girlhood.

Had she, though? asked an inner voice. Would a full-
grown woman have reacted the way she had reacted over
what to all intents and purposes was purely and simply
hearsay? Sam hadn't seen Nick and Dione together herself;
she only had Tim's word for it. Supposing he was lying?

She was grasping at straws, she told herself wearily. Tim
had no reason to lie. It was too late anyway.

The evening wore on, every minute an hour, every hour

a lifetime. Erin dreaded the night still to come, yet even that was going to be easier than the morning. He'd take care of it all, Nick had said, but there were things she had to see to herself. The packages still out in the car must be returned to their various points of origin for a start—embarrassing though it would be to do it. She would also book a seat on the next available flight to Heathrow while she was in town. Hopefully it would be before Monday. Flying home on what was to have been her wedding day would be too much to bear.

Despite everything, her heart leapt when the door opened again, sinking back into its pit when the visitor turned out to be Sam.

'Nick says you're going back home!' she burst out. 'You can't, Rin! I'm not staying here without you!'

Erin made a wry gesture. 'I'm afraid you have to. Even if Nick would allow it, I couldn't take you with me. It's going to be difficult enough as it is.'

'You don't *have* to go! Nick says it's your decision, not his. Everything will be all right again now you're not going to marry him. Things will just go back to the way they were.'

'They can't. Not now.' Erin could hardly bear to even think about it. 'It's no use, Sam. There's no way I can stay on here. You have to see that.'

'You could find somewhere else to live. I bet Mrs Marshall would help if you asked her.'

'Even if she could, I wouldn't want it,' Erin denied. 'The only way I'm ever going to be able to get over Nick is to go where I'm never likely to see him again.'

Samantha was silent for a moment, a variety of expressions chasing across her face. 'You still love him, don't you?' she said on a defeated note.

'Yes,' Erin admitted. 'I know I probably shouldn't, after what he's done, but I can't help it.'

'He hasn't.' Her sister's voice was so low it was scarcely audible. 'It was all Tim's idea.'

Eyes dark, heart plummeting to new depths, Erin said thickly, 'What was?'

'Telling you he'd seen them together. He knew I wanted to stop you from marrying Nick.'

'I see.' Erin struggled to contain the anger welling up inside her. 'Well, you certainly succeeded.'

'I'm sorry, Rin.' Sam looked on the verge of tears. 'I was so jealous of you! Nick's *my* uncle, but he wouldn't have bothered with me at all if you hadn't been there. He doesn't even like me!'

'That's nonsense!' Erin thrust everything else aside for the moment to go and put her arms around the girl, hugging her close. 'Of course he likes you, dummy! You've just been making it a bit difficult for him to show it, that's all.'

'I've ruined everything!' Sam was crying in earnest now. 'I'm really, really sorry, Rin.'

'Don't,' Erin pleaded. 'It's all right. I understand.'

'How can it be all right? You've told Nick you don't want to marry him now, and it's all my fault.' She lifted a tear-streaked face. 'Couldn't you say you'd made a mistake and you'd changed your mind again?'

Erin kept her tone carefully neutral. 'I don't think so. I've got a box of tissues in the bathroom. Sit down while I fetch them.'

The detachment was surface only. Reaching the bathroom, she stood for a moment or two to gather herself, aware that it was going to take everything she had to restrain the urge to hit out at the girl who had cost her everything she held dear.

Except that she hadn't, had she? came the unwelcome thought. Not wholly. If she had given Nick the opportunity to speak for himself, instead of simply accepting Sam's word, then none of this need have happened.

It took her several minutes of talking and cuddling to convince her sister that she bore no grudge.

'I'm as much to blame, if not more, for wading in the way I did,' she said. 'Love and trust are supposed to go hand in hand. Anyway,' she added, forcing a lighter note, 'it's time you were in bed. You still have school in the morning.'

'I'll not be having anything to do with Tim Wyman again, for certain!' Sam vowed. 'I wouldn't be surprised if Dione put him up to it to start with.'

The same thought had crossed Erin's mind. Not that it altered anything.

Sam looked back tentatively from the door. 'Do you really mean to go back home, Rin?'

'I have to,' she said.

Her sister nodded as if in resignation, and went, leaving Erin to face the effort of getting ready for bed herself.

She was lying there, far from sleep, when the door once more opened some immeasurable time later. Nick didn't switch on any lights, coming over to the bed as Erin lifted herself on an elbow.

'Sam told me what she told you,' he said. 'Did it occur to you to ask me if it was true?'

Erin shook her head, keeping a tight rein on her emotions. 'Not then. I was too busy saving face.' She hesitated, unable to see his expression all that clearly, and not at all certain why he was here. 'I'm sorry, Nick.'

'Sorry for believing it, or for telling me you'd changed your mind about marrying me?'

'Both.' A cautious warmth was beginning to uncurl deep inside her. 'I thought you might be relieved to be rid of me.'

'Did you now?'

'Yes.' She made an appealing gesture. 'I've behaved pretty appallingly all round.'

'You certainly have,' he agreed. 'Utterly outrageous from start to finish!'

'Most of it purely involuntary,' she claimed. 'You obviously bring out the worst in me.' She paused again, still not wholly sure. 'Am I forgiven?'

'For doubting me, yes. Not for what you've put me through these last few hours.'

'What have I put you through?' she whispered.

'Hell,' he said simply. 'I really thought I'd lost you.'

The warmth had permeated her whole body. 'It mattered that much?'

'More than anything I'd ever known.' He sat down on the edge of the mattress, taking her face between his hands to kiss her with a tenderness that spoke more loudly than any words. 'I love you, Erin. I've loved you since the first moment I saw you. Oh, I wouldn't let myself recognise it at first. I even managed to convince myself I was just being philanthropic, bringing you out here with Sam—for a little while, at any rate. Finding you in the pool that night finished me.'

'If you felt like that about me, why were you so rotten to me next morning?' she murmured, still finding it difficult to realise that everything was coming out right after all.

'Guilt,' he said. 'I'd not only taken a girl nearly half my age, I'd opened up a sex drive she wasn't capable of handling.'

'I was so!' Erin disputed. 'I was handling it just fine until you turned all holy on me!'

His lips curved. 'I remember. Beats an alarm clock any day of the week!'

'You thought it was someone else, though, didn't you?' she said, and saw the smile fade a little. 'It doesn't matter,' she tagged on swiftly. 'Really it doesn't.'

'Nothing that happened before I met you matters,' he

said on a roughened note. 'You're the only woman I want in my life.'

Erin widened her eyes at him. 'I was still a girl a minute ago.'

'Figuratively speaking.' He was smiling again, though a certain tension still lingered. 'I know what you feel for me is probably still little more than infatuation at present, but you'll have plenty of time to learn what love's really about when we're married. One thing I can't do is risk you falling for someone else.'

'As if I ever could,' she said softly. She put her hands to his face in turn, running the balls of her thumbs along the firm line of his jaw. 'It isn't just infatuation, Nick. I love you so much it hurts! If I'd gone back to England, I'd have spent the rest of my life pining for you. I can't wait to be married to you. And just to prove that sex isn't the only thing I'm interested in, I'm ready to stay celibate for the whole first year—well, a month, at any rate.'

Nick's laugh was good to hear, the light in his eyes good to see. 'You know there's as much chance of my taking you up on that as the two of us sprouting wings!'

'I thought it unlikely,' she admitted. She sobered again, to add with force, 'Don't you ever try telling me I don't know what love is really about again! I'm as capable of it as you are—probably more so because I'm a woman, and it's a well-known fact that women feel emotion far more deeply than men.'

'We might do a deal less talking about it, but that's the only difference.' Nick stroked back the tumbled hair from her face the way he had done that very first time, studying her as if to commit every last, minute feature to memory. 'You're lovely now, but you're going to be even more so in years to come. I want to paint you at every stage of your life—girl, wife, maybe mother too, in time.'

In not too much time if she had anything to do with it, thought Erin mistily, her cup overflowing.

'You know I'm...indisposed,' she added, coming down to earth again as Nick stood up to start removing his clothing.

'I hadn't forgotten,' he said. 'We've all the time in the world to make love. Tonight, I just want to hold you close.'

Erin relaxed again, secure in the knowledge that sex wasn't his only need either. The honeymoon could wait.

EPILOGUE

'I PRONOUNCE you husband and wife,' intoned the pastor, drawing recollective sighs from one or two members of the congregation.

Erin's prime reaction was one of relief. It had been a pretty hectic few days. Now, at last, she could relax, secure in the knowledge that last-minute hitches were a thing of the past. The dress fitted like a dream again, after Tessa's quick nip and tuck last night when the final trying-on session had revealed the loss of a pound or two. Just the reception to get through, then it would be time for bride and groom to be on their way.

'Where are you going?' piped up a voice as she made to follow Nick out into the aisle.

'Hush, now!' admonished Bella, holding the small, squirming figure firmly on her ample lap. 'Your mama and papa have to go and see Aunt Samantha and Uncle Alan sign the big book to say they married now.'

'We shan't be long,' promised Erin, turning back to direct a smile at the child. 'You stay with Bella, Ryan.'

'I'm thankful Sam decided against having him as a page-boy,' she murmured as she joined Nick. 'I think it could have proved a bit of a disaster.'

'I'm sure of it,' he returned drily. 'That son of ours is mischief personified!'

'No more than any other three-year-old,' she claimed, drawing a grin.

'I wouldn't want to take a bet on it. Lucky our first-born is so well-behaved.'

They were coming into the vestry. Erin sought and found

the diminutive figure of their daughter amidst the group of bridesmaids gathered about the happy couple. Pretty as a picture in her lilac and white crinoline dress, blonde hair cascading down her back, Francesca displayed a poise far in advance of her six and a half years. 'She been on this earth before,' Bella had declared more than once.

It seemed a lot less than eight years since she had sat where Sam was sitting now to sign the register, Erin reflected. At forty-two, Nick looked very little different from the man she had fallen in love with on sight, lean and fit as ever in the formal morning attire, dark hair showing the merest hint of silver at the temples.

They'd been wonderful years all round. Not totally without dispute, it had to be admitted, but then what married couple didn't have the occasional disagreement? What mattered was the balance achieved.

He had given her so much, not least the ability to express herself on canvas the way she had always yearned to do. While she would never match his talent, Miles Penhalligen had been impressed enough with her work to offer her a minor exhibition a couple of years ago, since when she had achieved a fair degree of success in her own right. Not the most important accomplishment of her life, but satisfying all the same.

The children were their joint pride and joy. Nick was a brilliant father, never too busy to spend time with them, just enough of a disciplinarian to counteract her own tendency towards over-indulgence at times. A brilliant lover still, too, came the thought, curving her lips into a reminiscent little smile. A good sex life might not be the only factor necessary to a happy marriage, but it surely helped.

'You've done a great job putting all this together,' Nick said quietly, viewing the serenely lovely face beneath the wide white brim of her hat.

'No more than you did for us,' she responded.

'Hardly on the same scale. Trust Sam to want the full works!' He paused, eyes reflective. 'Do you ever regret not having had the same?'

'Not for a minute,' Erin returned truthfully. 'My memories leave nothing to be desired. My life neither,' she added softly, and saw the greyness take on a deeper hue.

'Nor mine,' he said. 'No man could ask for more.'

MILLS & BOON®

Makes any time special

Enjoy a romantic novel from Mills & Boon®

Presents™ *Enchanted*™ *Temptation*®

Historical Romance™ *Medical Romance*™

MILLS & BOON®

Next Month's Romance Titles

♡

Each month you can choose from a wide variety of romance novels from Mills & Boon®. Below are the new titles to look out for next month from the Presents™ and Enchanted™ series.

Presents™

LOVER BY DECEPTION	Penny Jordan
THE SECRET MISTRESS	Emma Darcy
HAVING HIS BABIES	Lindsay Armstrong
ONE HUSBAND REQUIRED!	Sharon Kendrick
THE MARRIAGE QUEST	Helen Brooks
THE SEDUCTION BID	Amanda Browning
THE MILLIONAIRE'S CHILD	Susanne McCarthy
SHOTGUN WEDDING	Alexandra Sellers

Enchanted™

A NINE-TO-FIVE AFFAIR	Jessica Steele
LONE STAR BABY	Debbie Macomber
THE TYCOON'S BABY	Leigh Michaels
DATING HER BOSS	Liz Fielding
BRIDEGROOM ON LOAN	Emma Richmond
BABY WISHES AND BACHELOR KISSES	Valerie Parv
THERE GOES THE BRIDE	Renee Roszel
DADDY WOKE UP MARRIED	Julianna Morris

On sale from 4th June 1999

H1 9905

Available at most branches of WH Smith, Tesco, Asda, Martins, Borders, Easons, Volume One/James Thin and most good paperback bookshops

Perfect Summer

The perfect way to relax this summer!

Four stories from best selling
Mills & Boon® authors

JoAnn Ross

Vicki Lewis Thompson

Janice Kaiser

Stephanie Bond

*Enjoy the fun, the drama
and the excitement!*

Published 21 May 1999

*Available at most branches of WH Smith, Tesco, Asda,
Martins, Borders, Easons, Volume One/James Thin
and most good paperback bookshops*

4 Books
and a surprise gift!

We would like to take this opportunity to thank you for reading this Mills & Boon® book by offering you the chance to take FOUR more specially selected titles from the Presents™ series absolutely FREE! We're also making this offer to introduce you to the benefits of the Reader Service™ —

- ★ FREE home delivery
- ★ FREE gifts and competitions
- ★ FREE monthly Newsletter
- ★ Books available before they're in the shops
- ★ Exclusive Reader Service discounts

Accepting these FREE books and gift places you under no obligation to buy; you may cancel at any time, even after receiving your free shipment. Simply complete your details below and return the entire page to the address below. *You don't even need a stamp!*

YES! Please send me 4 free Presents books and a surprise gift. I understand that unless you hear from me, I will receive 6 superb new titles every month for just £2.40 each, postage and packing free. I am under no obligation to purchase any books and may cancel my subscription at any time. The free books and gift will be mine to keep in any case.

P9EB

Ms/Mrs/Miss/Mr ....Initials ....

BLOCK CAPITALS PLEASE

Surname...

Address..

....

....Postcode ....

Send this whole page to:
THE READER SERVICE, FREEPOST CN81, CROYDON, CR9 3WZ
(Eire readers please send coupon to: P.O. BOX 4546, DUBLIN 24.)

mps MAILING PREFERENCE SERVICE

MILLS & BOON®

Makes any time special™

By Request

Bestselling themed romances brought back to you by popular demand

Each month By Request brings you three full-length novels in one beautiful volume featuring the best of the best.

So if you missed a favourite Romance the first time around, here is your chance to relive the magic from some of our most popular authors.

Look out for
***Her Baby Secret* in June 1999**
featuring Lynne Graham,
Jacqueline Baird and Day Leclaire

Available at most branches of WH Smith, Tesco, Asda, Martins, Borders, Easons, Volume One/James Thin and most good paperback bookshops